The Greatest

Sex
· TIPS ·

in the **World**®

by
Julie Peasgood

Illustrated by
Tracy Staskevich

Public Eye Publications

A Public Eye Publications Book

www.thegreatestintheworld.com

Illustrations:
Tracy Staskevich
www.tracystaskevich.co.uk

Cover design:
pentacorbig: book & information graphic design
www.pentacorbig.co.uk

Typesetting:
Bloomfield Ltd.

Copy editor:
Bronwyn Robertson
www.theartsva.com

Series creator/editor:
Steve Brookes

This first edition published in 2007 by
Public Eye Publications, PO Box 3182,
Stratford-upon-Avon, Warwickshire CV37 7XW

Text and Illustrations Copyright © 2007 – Public Eye Publications

'The Greatest in the World' Copyright © 2004 – Anne Brookes

A CIP catalogue record for this book is available from the British Library
ISBN 9781-905151-25-7

Printed and bound by Biddles Books Limited, King's Lynn, Norfolk PE30 4LS

To my wonderful husband
Patrick Pearson.

Thank you so much for your wit
and your inspired way with words.

This book would not have been written without
your love, support, faith, patience, sense of fun –
and collaboration (in every way!)

Contents

Foreword

Julie's easy way with words flows through this compelling sex guide like fine wine. With a wicked sense of humour she educates on all matters sexual and continually surprises the reader with fascinating sex trivia. Do you know that Dr John Harvey Kellogg invented his cornflakes as a libido suppressant, or that it was commonplace at the end of the 19th Century for doctors to masturbate female patients to orgasm to treat sexual desire, known then as 'hysteria'? Julie does.

This guide is perfect bedside reading for couples, addressing men's needs as well as women's, with lessons for him in how to exercise his pelvic floor muscles for sexual benefits. Yes, men have them too. And tricky topics are thoroughly tackled from faked orgasms to having sex during periods to vagina size issues. In between you'll find every tip you need to improve your sex life and boost your orgasmic potential from 'good' to 'oh my God!'.

An air of confident authority prevails throughout, but reading *The Greatest Sex Tips* still feels as comfortable as having a chat with an old friend down at the local pub. If only all friends were so well-informed ...

Sarah x

Sarah Hedley
Editor
Scarlet Magazine

"There are many people who have questions about sex and this book provides some honest and often fascinating answers. Julie has written an informative, frank and humorous guide which gives great tips for improving your sex life. Packed with techniques you may have tried and others you'd never dreamed of, this is a really enjoyable read for anyone looking to spice up their love life or simply find out more about sex."

Dr Catherine Hood
Sexual health & relationship expert

"Quirky, clever and packed with enough tantalising facts and stats to make you the star of a hundred dinner parties."

Tracey Cox
Sex & relationships expert and best-selling author

"Use this book! I very rarely meet people who are totally satisfied with their love life, yet most of us guys make little effort to improve things. Here's a great, easy way to get things going in the right direction – once a week stay in bed with your lover and try one new tip from this book. Before you know it you will have re-energised your love making!"

Mimo Antonucci
Founder of www.sensualessentials.com

"Anyone who knows Julie knows that she is one incredibly sexy woman and now we know why! Scandalous, delightful this book is a must read for anyone who prefers being awake during sex and smiling after it. I was supposed to be getting ready for an afternoon of work but after reading this book I think I'm off to play …"

Jenni Trent Hughes
Relationship counsellor

A few words from Julie …

I've always refused to believe that our sex lives have to become boring, or even completely disintegrate, as we settle down in a relationship. Don't get me wrong – I do acknowledge that the steamy euphoria of the initial six months has to calm down, so you can put your knickers back on and pay the bills. I just don't accept sinking into the inevitability of cosy slippers and cups of tea, when we may also yearn for a spark of passion to relight our fire.

This book has been written for anyone who wants to put some fun into their lovemaking and broaden their sexual horizons – regardless of age, sexual orientation, whether you've been in a relationship for years or are newly enjoying each other. I've sought out tips that I hope will inform, inspire and ultimately improve what is such an important aspect of our lives – and they're all tried and tested.

Sex is universal – we wouldn't be here without it – and there's always room for improvement. We're very focussed today on personal development – we're constantly being urged to move out of our comfort zones and to set goals for our careers, fitness levels, finances, weight-loss … why don't we have some fun and set a few for our sex lives too?

I hope you find this guide amusing, enlightening, reassuring, and of course stimulating – and I also hope you have as much fun reading it as I've had putting it all together!

With love,

Julie

"What a spectacular start to the final of Strictly Come Kissing … "

chapter 1
Kiss and make out

The first sexually intimate act most of us experience is a kiss. Whether it's behind the school bike-sheds, in a darkened shop doorway or, like mine, in the seductive environment of our local fish finger factory, that heady excitement of another's lips pressed against yours is wonderful ... if you're lucky.

In *Gone with the Wind* Clark Gable declares to Vivien Leigh "You should be kissed, and often, and by someone who knows how". Yes please, Rhett. There are many talented kissers in the world, who've elevated this simple act into an art form, but sadly there are others whose technique leaves a lot to be desired.

If you think you've been neglecting your snogging skills – or you know someone who has – it's worth polishing them up. The lips are a major erogenous zone, in fact practitioners of tantric sex advocate a gentle sucking of the lips, crediting them with a hotline to the genitals.

Research by the Marriage Guidance Council indicates that when a relationship deteriorates, kissing is one of the first things to go – but if you make an effort to put it back on the menu, it can rekindle the romance and emotional bond between you.

Even if you're completely satisfied with your partner, you may still be longing for more opportunities to pucker up – a top psychotherapist recently revealed that the number of times an average couple kiss is four-and-a-half pecks a day. That's Good Morning, Hello, Goodbye and Goodnight (which presumably lasts a bit longer and accounts for the half). Read on for some lip-smacking how's, why's, do's and don'ts.

Upside down canoodle

I know this might sound a little strange, but it's good for a giggle if nothing else. (Hell, if Kirsten Dunst can enjoy it with Spiderman, who are we to criticise?) Best performed on the bed or floor, one partner's lips are upside-down to the other partner's, so your mouths are top lip to bottom lip. Added bonus: if the person on top crawls forward you're in a perfect 69 position — could be handy.

Kiss me, honey honey ...

Try planting tiny delicate kisses all over your loved one's face, to gently wake them up in the morning. The secret is to make the touch of your lips as soft and tender as possible, and take your time — this isn't one to attempt with the clock ticking, but it's a magical way to start the day.

8 reasons to banish the stiff upper lip

1. Ann Summers has compiled a survey of Britain's sexiest turn-ons, and a good old-fashioned kiss comes in at Number One.

2. Dentists suggest that it's good for the teeth. Kissing can help prevent plaque build-up, because the saliva we produce reduces the natural acids in the mouth.

3. A kiss is quite a complex operation, requiring no less than 20 muscles working in harmony, and burning around 150 calories an hour.

4. Scientific studies have proved it can help reduce skin blemishes and rashes.

5. There's an International Kissing Day on July 6th, so that's a tailor-made excuse to grab Debbie from Accounts and show her your credentials.

6. France has over 20 different words for it.

7. A recent study suggests that people who give their partner a goodbye kiss before going to work have, on average, higher incomes than those who don't!

8. The world's longest recorded smacker took place in New York in 2005, and lasted 30 hours, 59 minutes and 27 seconds. (Now that's what I call a kiss.)

Merci please

If the idea of French kissing, for either you or your partner, seems as distant as St. Tropez, experiment with kissing concentrating only on the lips — no tongues allowed. Take lots of time to lick, nibble, suck and really relish the sensation. Not only will it send waves of pleasure coursing through to your nether regions, but it's a clever way of making you crave deeper, more intimate French kissing again — as in 'abstinence makes the tongue grow fonder'.

12 lip-action 'Do's and Don'ts'

Do ... clean your teeth — and your tongue whilst you're at it (pink and smooth wins over white and fuzzy). And don't forget to floss to ensure a super-sweet mouth.

Do ... vary the tempo. Start slow and sensual, then get more urgent and intense as your passion builds — much more exciting to be a bit unpredictable.

Do ... gently hold and caress your partner's head or face as you're locking lips.

Do ... tell each other, and demonstrate, how you like to be kissed. Feedback is vital in order to really get it right — and watch each other's reactions too. If your loved one is blissed out, motionless and their eyes are still closed when you pull back, you can safely assume you got it right.

Do ... grab every chance to enjoy a quick clinch — and make it a habit you keep up.

Do ... make it last. Long, heady, toe-curling French kisses are good for the soul — possibly why they're also known as soul kisses.

Don't … dive straight in and start playing tonsil hockey. Invite your lover in gently by parting your lips a little. Then trace the tip of your tongue around their lips – and explore a little further before you finally intertwine tongues.

Don't … just think of kissing as a prelude to other things – it's valuable in its own right.

Don't … smoke. Try to give up if you possibly can – for every health reason going. Ashtray breath also rates high on the kissing turn-offs list.

Don't … slobber over your partner. Swallow any saliva that's surplus to requirements.

Don't … even go there if you have a cold sore. Caused by the herpes simplex virus, cold sores are highly contagious and passed on through infected saliva, so steer clear of smooching until they're past tense.

Don't … forget to look deep into each other's eyes in between kisses – and never underestimate the importance of the Kiss.

The kiss of life

It's a harsh truth guys, but in the snogging stakes you're falling short of the mark. Apparently 95% of young women are not satisfied with their quota when it comes to kissing – and the older ones aren't grinning from ear to ear either. Basically, kissing is to most women what blow jobs are to men – it's one of the things we love most, but don't usually get enough of. Become a champion at delivering great lip service and you've just about got it made – it's a guaranteed knicker-wetter. What's more, many women also believe that men who can't or don't kiss are rubbish in bed, so please double our doses – or you might never find out just how good it makes us feel …

"Are you lost, honey?"

chapter 2
A grand opening

The ancient Indian sex manual, the *Kama Sutra*, identifies three types of vagina. According to size, women are either a deer, a mare or – wait for it – an elephant. I know there's a charming, modern expression that if a woman is rather roomy down below, making love to her is like 'chucking a sausage down Oxford Street' – they obviously weren't averse to the odd insult back in the 4th Century either.

Vaginas are created in all shapes, sizes, and colours. The average human vagina is about 4 inches (10 cm) long, and is a muscular tube that expands or contracts to accommodate a finger, penis, or a baby.

The term 'vagina' is often used to describe the female genitalia but it is, in fact, only the passageway connecting the external bits to the uterus, with the cervix at its upper end. The proper name for our private parts is pudenda (not often used), vulva (most often used), or split beaver (only kidding).

Women can be shy about their vulvas – they're not normally on show, except to our lovers (and sometimes not even then if we're very self conscious). Inner labia are often a source of potential embarrassment – some are dark and wrinkly, some are small and pale, some hang down, some have one lip longer than the other. Whatever your particular configuration, trust me – there are no genital deformities, only variations on a theme. Certain tribeswomen in Africa even take pains (literally) to weight their labia down, to develop a desirable 7 inch (18 cm) dangle.

Whatever turns you on I say – *viva la vulva!*

Let's hear it for the clit …

The clitoris has 8,000 nerve endings (twice as many as the penis) and is the most sensitive organ in the human body; in fact it's even more responsive than our tongues. Made up of eighteen parts — some visible, some hidden — it's also the only body part designed solely to give pleasure to its owner.

The bare essentials

Show off your booty with a Hollywood. Whether your preferred method is to wax (aagh!) or shave (get partner to do it?) the overall porn-star effect is powerfully erotic. There's something so illicit about being completely exposed, and the total lack of hair makes your whole vulva even more sensitive. If you feel that taking it all off is just too 'little girl-like' though, you could opt for a Brazilian, and leave a narrow landing strip above your bare labia. Alternatively try the American favourite, the "Tiffany Box" — all pubes removed except for a tiny square, which is then dyed that famous shade of duck-egg blue … Who's for Breakfast?

A close shave

For an easy, pain-free path to pubic grooming, try a specialist shaving system such as the Smoothshave Intimate Area Shaver. It's a nifty little battery operated number that's designed specifically for use on stubble, promising to leave skin as smooth as a baby's bum — in fact the only accompaniment needed is baby talc, which makes it feel surprisingly safe and simple to use. If you're starting from scratch you'll also need something like their Shavy Femini Trimmer to cut back thicker pubes first, as the Intimate Area Shaver is best used for daily maintenance. (Great for guys, too — see *Supersize me*, page 32.)

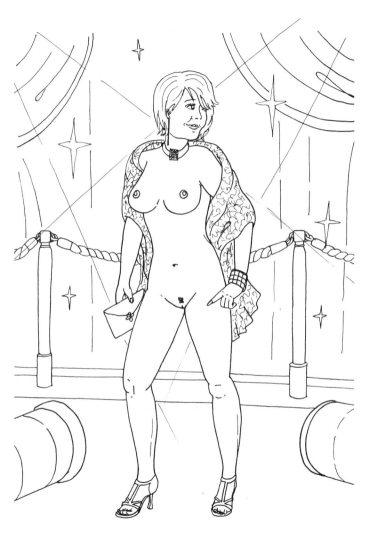

"Tiffany, Tiffany, over here!"

Little Miss Muff(et)

On the other hand, if you prefer not to prune your bush, then
I have it on very good authority that some men find a couple
of stray pubes poking out of your panties to be a massive turn-on.
Just one or two little 'spider's legs' is apparently all it takes ...

Taking the curse off things

Lots of women report feeling extra horny when they're having their period. This could be due to a number of reasons: see-sawing hormone levels can make you bolder sexually, nerve endings are at their most responsive at this time, and you may be less uptight about getting pregnant, if that's an issue (although this can still happen).

As an orgasm is also a great cure for period pains and cramps, there's no reason why you shouldn't make love, providing neither of you is put off or worried about any potential mess — keep the wet wipes handy just in case, and maybe place a towel underneath you to save the sheets. Use some lube if you've just removed a tampon, and it's better to choose a position where he's on top — your blood flow is likely to be reduced when you're lying down. It also helps to pop a pillow under your bottom to raise your pelvis.

Ideally wait until the really heavy days are over, but if you want the freedom of having sex at any point in your cycle, then it might be worth trying a menstrual cup, such as Instead. This is an innovative alternative to tampons and pads, and inserted as easily as a diaphragm (though please note it isn't a method of contraception). It allows clean, comfortable sex during your period, and as it's discreet, you can both just forget it's that time of the month.

Elusive but effusive

One theory about the G-spot is that it's actually the root of the clitoris. Another is that it protects the urethra during intercourse, which is why it's also called the urethral sponge. Since its discovery in the 1940s by the German gynaecologist Ernst Grafenberg, the G-spot has spawned various theories and aroused heated debate. Most women today agree that it certainly arouses something – however, you need to find it first and that isn't always easy.

It's best to locate your G-spot when you're sitting down or squatting, but you can lie on your stomach or on your back with your legs in the air – whichever suits you most. Place your palm face down on your vulva, and insert a lubricated finger inside yourself, crooking it forward towards your pubic bone. You're looking for a swelling directly behind this bone, that's about a couple of inches (3–5cms) inside your vagina. It's a pronounced, spongy lump, around the size of a bean, on the front wall (the side closest to your tummy) and it feels more ridged and bumpy in texture than the surrounding vaginal walls. (Don't confuse it with your cervix, which is smooth and, in the words of sexpert Tracey Cox, "feels like the very round end of a nose".)

You'll know when you've struck gold because you'll instantly feel like you want to pee. This is because the G-spot shares a nerve with the bladder, and it's a completely normal feeling – which will subside. If you're having trouble locating the exact spot, you might want to get your partner in on the act, or play around with a specially curved dildo or vibrator. It's also easier to find after you've had an orgasm, because it gets slightly harder and increases noticeably in size, becoming more like a walnut than a bean.

No matter how aroused they are, some women don't find the G-spot does anything for them, and some still dispute its very existence. Others find it so intense that they go to heaven and back with a monumental climax – and a lucky minority also ejaculate a slightly milky fluid (which isn't urine) if they reach orgasm this way. To find out how, see *Going with the flow*, page 50 – and enjoy the search!

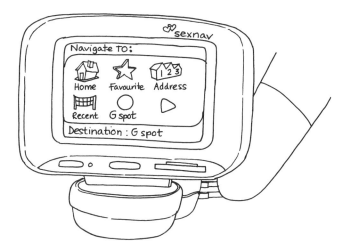

"Darling, I think we're going to need some more dye."

My plaice or yours?

Did you know that a man is actually partially responsible for his partner's smell down below? Sperm is highly alkaline and it causes the pH – acid/alkali – levels inside the vagina to rise, allowing unhealthy bacteria to take hold. Usually the body quickly restores the balance, especially when the sperm is familiar (as it is with a regular partner). It's trickier to correct, though, if a woman has unprotected sex with one or more new partners, and can often result in a strong 'fishy' smell.

Matching collar and cuffs

For the first time ever a hair dye has been specially created for the nether regions. The brainchild of Betty Beauty Ltd., its safe, non-drip formula is intended for use around our most sensitive area, with a range of colours including hot pink and platinum blonde. It's great for guys too (OK maybe not the fuchsia) but it's effective for covering any unsightly grey pubes, or to match the thatch on top.

Now you really can get away with calling yourself a natural blonde ...

Smile please!

Treat your hidden lips to a slick of minty gloss with Flower Power Lip Balm Orgasm Booster. With a consistency similar to conventional lip balms, it warms your pussy, tingles your clit, and makes it difficult to think of anything other than getting a good seeing-to as quickly as possible. A product that does what it says on the tin.

Get a grip

Many years ago in Bangkok, I found myself in the privileged position of watching an accomplished Thai dancer shoot ping-pong balls from her vagina. She then progressed to smoking a cigar, using only the iron grip of her pelvic floor muscles. This is not easy. I know because I've tried. My horrified partner found me in our hotel room with one of his finest Havana's protruding from my pudenda – and things were never quite the same again.

Strong pelvic floor muscles are crucial for optimum sexual health. Otherwise known as PC or Kegel muscles, they support all the pelvic organs, and are the ones that contract during orgasm. Originally pioneered by Dr Arnold Kegel in the 1940s (who discovered their sensual side-effects when he helped women overcome incontinence problems), they're the same muscles we use to stop ourselves peeing mid-flow. So not only will well-toned PCs give you greater bladder control, they'll also improve the frequency and force of your orgasms – and do wonders for keeping you tight down below (especially after childbirth).

The extra bonus is that you can discreetly squeeze and release, when and where you like – start with 25 clenches, twice a day, and build up to 50, holding each time for a count of two. If you're not good at remembering though, and only end up doing a random clench at the bus stop occasionally, you can invest in a device like the Natural Contours Energie Kegel Exerciser for a proper workout. Either way, consciously exercising your Kegels will enhance every aspect of your sex life, giving your man a vaginal embrace he's not likely to forget. You'll be playing ping-pong before you know it.

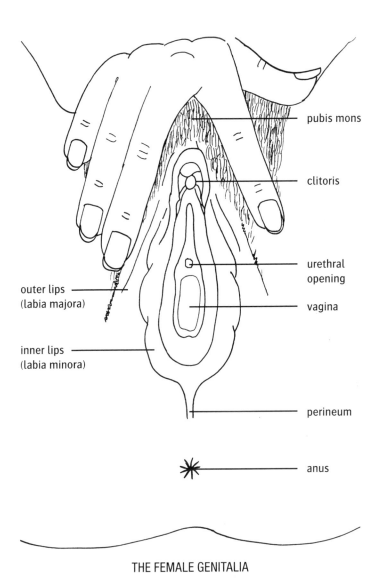

pubis mons

clitoris

urethral
opening

outer lips
(labia majora)

vagina

inner lips
(labia minora)

perineum

anus

THE FEMALE GENITALIA

chapter 3
A handler's guide

Penis size varies enormously, but the average range is between 2 to 4 inches (5–10 cm) at rest and 5 to 7 inches (13–18 cm) when standing to attention, with an erect circumference of 4½ inches (11½ cm). I'm launching straight into measurements here, because numerous surveys suggest that men are just a tad preoccupied with the size of their members. It seems almost all of you – regardless of sexual orientation – wish you had a bigger one. (Stop looking for that tape measure.)

As Sarah Hedley writes in *Sex by Numbers,* "sex researcher Alfred Kinsey conducted a survey of the penis in the 1940s and concluded that the average length was 6 5/16 in (16 cm). However, it seems many of Kinsey's subjects were stretching the truth (and the measurements), adding an extra ½ in (1 cm) or so when they were left alone to mark down their length. Bless."

The irony is most women aren't too fussed, in fact 98% of us are turned on by our lover's penis, whatever its size. As the average length of the female vagina is just 4 inches (10 cm) with only the first third being really sensitive, you don't have to be hung like a donkey to be a great lover – we quite like you at the shallow end sometimes. (Equally, if you *are* hung like a donkey and reading this, I'm sure you've given rides to some very appreciative admirers – I bet your toffee apples are a sight to behold too.)

Like vulvas, penises come in all shapes, sizes, and colours – and you know what? They're all works of art.

Measuring up

I have it on very good authority that blokes are never quite sure exactly how to measure their manhoods, so here's the correct method, according to American doctor Harold Reed, MD:

- While standing, make your penis erect.
- Angle your penis down until it is parallel to the floor.
- Set a ruler against your pubic bone just above the base of your penis, and measure to the tip.
- Now wash the ruler.

The hotspots

It's a good idea to be familiar with the supersensitive bits of a man's member. Generally the head of the penis is much more responsive than the base. Most supercharged of all are:

Glans – the head or 'helmet' – choc-full of nerve endings (many more than the shaft). Permanently on view if a man is circumcised, in uncircumcised men it can be seen when the penis is erect or with the foreskin rolled back.

Coronal rim – the tender rim of the glans. Also known as the crown (hence the Crown Jewels?).

Frenulum – the ultra-sensitive strand of skin joining the head and shaft, on the underside of the penis. High-ranking erogenous zone.

Shaft – the main body of the penis which fills up with blood, and hardens during arousal.

Scrotum – the soft, wrinkly pouch which protects the testicles, as they work their socks off to produce around 300 million sperm a day. (Each ejaculation spills between 200 and 600 million of them!)

Perineum – the area between the balls and the anus – also a major erogenous zone.

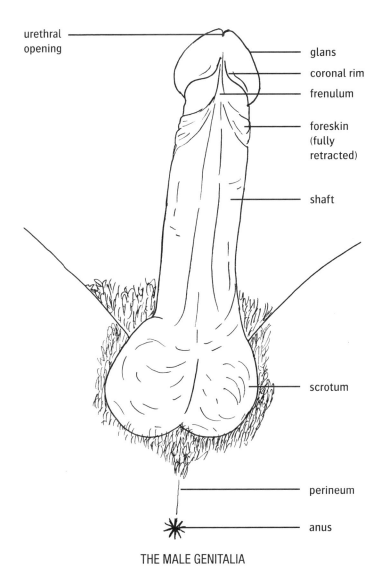

urethral opening

glans

coronal rim

frenulum

foreskin (fully retracted)

shaft

scrotum

perineum

anus

THE MALE GENITALIA

Disposable dong

The human penis is huge in relation to the rest of the male anatomy and is, in fact, one of the largest organs amongst the world's primates. OK, so the blue whale has a weapon that can measure up to three and a half metres, with the African elephant coming in at two metres, but good old Homo sapiens still manages to knock spots off the gorilla, with its meagre two inch offering – when erect. Only a barnacle has a bigger knob relative to its body size than Man, though it does enjoy the unique privilege of being able to throw it away every year and grow a new one.

Glisten up

We've all got used to the idea of men using moisturisers for a healthy facial glow – why not extend this to your penis? Women love a velvety smooth shaft, so grease your pole with a good body lotion or massage oil. It'll have the same beneficial effect – and you'll have more fun applying it!

Supersize me

OK guys, listen up. If you still believe that bigger is better (and it's not necessarily) you can give yourselves *instant* length by cutting back the hair from around the base of your penis. The effect is surprisingly impressive, giving the illusion that you're a good inch longer. Trim carefully with nail scissors, or use an intimate area shaver which is great for backs, sacks and cracks (and for shaving heads too). Go on, pinch an inch – who cares if it's all done with mirrors?

Seeds for seed

The amount of semen produced in an average ejaculation is one to two teaspoons, but the volume and potency vary according to the age and general health of the individual. The frequency of orgasm affects quantity too – you'll notice a difference if you hold back for a day or two as opposed to bashing one out every few hours.

You can stock up your sperm supplies by increasing fluid intake and eating foods rich in zinc, which is essential for sperm formation, prostate health and the production of testosterone. Good sources include pumpkin seeds, pine nuts, red meat, eggs, and wheatgerm.

Willy nilly

If you want to be the stiffest, most super-charged stud on the block, then steer clear of excessive beer and cigarettes. A couple of fags can quickly knock out a third of blood flow to the penis, and beer doesn't tick any boxes either – causing prostate difficulties as well as brewer's droop. A study in Hawaii of more than 6,500 men, revealed some prostate gland problems after shock/horror – even just *three* bottles of beer a month! Beer stimulates secretion of the hormone prolactin, which is linked with a diminished sex drive and possible impotence, so go a little easy on the pints.

Package deal

Bollocks, nuts, gonads, goolies, plums – call them what you will, but handle with care. A good starting point with your man's balls is to imagine you're cradling eggs (unboiled!) and if he's happy, take it from there. Use flavoured lube for a silky smooth fondle, then progress onto licking and teabagging (gently sucking a whole testicle in your mouth). And whatever you do, don't bite …

Rising to the occasion

There's a funny story about an actor, famous in the 70s, who was always cast as villains or 'hard men'. This might have had something to do with the fact that he was something of a hard man himself – in more ways than one. Not only was he known for his acting and his criminal exploits, but he developed a novel party piece, which he showed off to great acclaim in the pub.

Being blessed with an absolutely enormous cock, plus pelvic floor muscles made of steel, he could reputedly hang *four* half-pint tankards on his proud and rigid member. Rumour has it, he was even summoned to entertain a certain member of the Royal Family with the trick – but then again, that could be a bone of contention ...

PC world

The road to multiple male orgasms is lined with several options. You could spend years studying the Kama Sutra, Tantric, or Taoist scriptures, you could follow up the tip mentioned in *The second coming* on page 44. You could risk personal injury (and smash a lot of beer glasses) trying that last trick, or you could start today with the most practical option – exercising your PC muscles.

These are the same pelvic floor muscles, and the same exercises (called Kegels), that women do to tone up vaginally (see *Get a grip*, page 27). You can identify which muscles they are, by stopping your urine mid-flow. They also enable you to 'lift' your penis when erect, and they contract when you climax – so strengthening them will make your orgasms more powerful.

Not only will you have a firmer erection to wave in her direction, but you'll be able to train yourself to stop on the brink of ejaculation, and enjoy the *sensation* of an orgasm in your brain, without actually shooting your load. Meaning you can also make love for longer, which coupled with your new super-stiffy, could make you rather popular.

To become a Sexual God, first stop the stream of urine mid-flow next time you have a pee. Then continue 'drawing in' these PC muscles and hold for a few seconds (keeping your thigh, back and abdominal muscles relaxed). You're aiming to start with 10 contractions, lasting a couple of seconds each, until you gradually build up to a set of 50. The goal is to do a couple of sets each day, so keep varying the speed to stop yourself getting bored, and whenever you have to queue anywhere use it as an opportunity to squeeze away. No one will have any idea what you're up to – unless you start to show off in the pub of course ...

Free willy

Ditching your underpants (i.e. 'going commando' or 'freeballing') is becoming increasingly fashionable. Some men are doing it on a daily basis, others are swinging free semi-regularly, but it's gaining in popularity all the time. Biggest advantages are that it's better for your fertility as your testicles aren't restricted by anything (tight underwear decreases sperm count) and it could increase the sensitivity of your penis. Your partner may also find it sexy to discover your dangly bits let loose – with easy access for a quick fondle – in fact it rates as Number 36 on Ann Summers' compilation of the 100 sexiest turn-ons. Not to mention that it avoids VPL (plus there's a lot less laundry).

When girls go commando it's sometimes known as 'freebuffing' and it'll certainly get you noticed – especially if you practise your leg-crossing skills.

Stress solution

Semen could have anti-depressant qualities (and no, that doesn't mean we want to swallow it three times a day). Tests have revealed that it contains a neurotransmitter called dopamine, which makes us feel happy, fulfilled – and all warm and fuzzy. It's also indicated that women who have condom-free sex with one regular partner, have lower levels of depression. (Oh, go on then big boy, bring it on ...)

Some journeys are just harder than others.

chapter 4
Coming to the point

The word orgasm stems from the Greek 'orgaein', meaning 'to swell' or 'to be excited and lustful'. The dictionary defines it as 'the most intense point during sexual excitement, characterised by extremely pleasurable sensations with involuntary contractions of the genital muscles, accompanied by ejaculation of semen in the male'.

This ejaculation exits the body at 28mph, so it won't lose you any points on your licence, although it is undoubtedly impressive. What's possibly even more amazing, as Jonathan Margolis tells us in *'O' The Intimate History of the Orgasm*, is that "in the average lifetime, a man produces 14 gallons of ejaculate, enough to fill the fuel tank of the average-sized family car". *Seriously* impressive (and a carbon neutral emission).

Us girls don't do so badly either – OK, it might take us longer to get there, but when we do, the results are dramatic. Our climaxes last from 12 to 107 seconds, compared to a man's 10 to 13 seconds, we can have multiple orgasms, and a small percentage of us even produce our own female ejaculate – more of which later.

An intense orgasm can provide a blissful release of mental and physical tension, flooding our systems with oxytocin, so we're suffused with feelings of love, warmth and tenderness. Small wonder then that we all strive for the summit, the peak, the 'Big O'. We may know countless ways to enjoy one – or maybe it's something we're not sure we've ever actually experienced (in which case skip this and go immediately to *Chapter 5 – Going it alone*). Wherever you're coming from, here's to your point of no return – may the force be with you.

Cold feet

A recent orgasm study in the Netherlands found that having cold feet prevented many people from climaxing. Keeping socks on in bed is normally one of the biggest no-no's, but both men and women found it easier to have an orgasm when their feet were warm and toasty. Sales of fluffy bedsocks could rocket.

A little list of Big O benefits (as if you needed one):

1. Forget botox – plenty of orgasms can make us look up to 10 years younger.

2. An orgasm is reputed to be the equivalent in exercise of a five-mile jog, meaning it's giving us a good cardiovascular workout by raising the heart rate, and improving overall muscle tone and circulation.

3. It's been suggested that as frequent male orgasm drains the body of seminal fluid, it can help a man avoid both congestive prostatis (inflammation of the prostate gland) and prostate cancer.

4. Sex is actually a beauty treatment. Scientific tests have revealed that when women make love they produce the hormone oestrogen, which makes hair shiny and keeps skin smooth and glowing.

5. The British Medical Journal has stated that the more orgasms you have, the longer you're likely to live. Apparently men who climax twice a week are half as likely to die prematurely as men who only climax once a month.

6. Feel-good endorphins are released when we climax – reducing both blood pressure and stress levels.

A helping hand

Let's face it, whoever designed the female anatomy needs to go back to the drawing board and move the clit down a bit. Granted, there are certain fortunate females who have a very large clitoris, or one that's extremely close to their vagina, but this is not the case for most women. Extensive research has revealed that only 20% of women orgasm through penetrative sex alone, and they're probably already very aroused, or receiving enough stimulation to their clits (from the thrusting or grinding of intercourse) to enable them to climax.

So in a nutshell, the clitoris is where it's at. Big-time. Whether we have a clitoral, vaginal, blended, G-spot, U-spot, A-spot, or a 2-hour-can't-speak-coherently orgasm (alright, so I made that last one up), you can bet your bottom dollar that our clits are involved somewhere along the line. To quote Ian Kerner in his book *She Comes First* "The clitoris is the powerhouse of pleasure. Any sex therapist will tell you that the number one complaint they hear over and over from women is of an inability to experience orgasm during penis-vagina intercourse ... think *clitorally*, rather than *vaginally* ... focus on *stimulation* as opposed to *penetration*."

Please don't get me wrong – I'm not saying women don't enjoy penetration – far from it – just let's not undervalue the real star of the show.

"Ladies and gentlemen, please welcome, the star of the show …"

The second coming

Back in the 60s the ground-breaking American sex researchers, Masters and Johnson, alleged that orgasm and ejaculation were two biologically independent processes, and one can take place without the other. What this means is that multiple climaxes aren't just reserved for the fairer sex – all you men out there can train yourselves to be multi-orgasmic too. You can have an amazing sensation of orgasm in your brains, without actually spurting – until you want to (see also *PC world*, page 34).

There is another approach that has tons of anecdotal evidence to endorse it. We know that massaging the prostate with a finger can enhance a man's orgasm (see *Prostate milking*, page 90), but progressing on from this is the concept of a separate internal or 'male P-Spot' orgasm, which doesn't depend on ejaculation either, and is produced by massaging the prostate with a stimulator.

There are lots of devices on the market for doing this, but the most widely publicised is the Aneros. It's a simple plastic device, not much bigger than a finger, with a curly T-bar to rest nicely up against the perineum (and to avoid any risk of it disappearing upwards).

Using lots of lube, the Aneros is inserted into the anus, and deep breathing is advised – to allow the body to become accustomed to the sensation. The user then controls its movement by rhythmically contracting and relaxing the sphincter muscles, causing the Aneros to 'stroke' the prostate, which creates very satisfying sensations. Not only are the PC muscles getting exercised (which helps tone the prostate) but with practice, it's possible for men to obtain 'full body', non-ejaculatory orgasms this way. Best of all, they can last for up to a minute, there's no limit as to how many – and all without batteries!

The penis doesn't even have to come to the party. It can do – it's possible, and pleasurable, to wear the device during intercourse (and ejaculation will be more profuse) – but the prostate is the main player.

There is a leap of faith required here, particularly for straight men, who may at first be wary of inserting anything, but the thought of being able to have several orgasms independent of – and even superior to – ejaculation, sounds pretty wild.

How was it for you?

Just about all of us have faked an orgasm during intercourse, and anyone who says they haven't is either incredibly lucky or telling porkies! (In fact statistics in a recent UK study found the number of female fibbers to be as high as 80%.) Blokes fake it too, although it's obviously harder for them to disguise the evidence (or lack of it), but women are definitely the main culprits, and there could be a number of reasons:

1. You want your partner to feel they're great in bed, and you don't want to hurt their feelings, so you're reluctant to admit that you're nowhere near coming in the foreseeable future.

2. You feel like you're 'failing' if you don't have an orgasm.

3. You're exhausted, and maybe if you pretend, then you can get it over with and go to sleep.

4 You just don't have the time. There's a sale at IKEA and then it's *Big Brother* ...

5. Because you can. Whether you stage a screaming, face-contorting, Oscar-winning performance, or settle for some heavy breathing and gentle moans, it's not difficult to get away with – but ultimately you're not doing yourself any favours. See the next tip for some reasons why you shouldn't go there.

Coming clean

Faking it is not a great idea. If your partner thinks they're getting it right, and that all it takes is a few frenzied thrusts to transport you to ecstasy, how are they ever going to discover what really works for you? They don't stand a chance of learning to pleasure you properly, and you run the risk of getting locked into a sexual lie that's difficult to get out of.

Not being honest about your needs can only lead to frustration and resentment. Talk to each other – be open and frank about what you like, but always be sensitive. It might not be an easy conversation, but it's worth it. This needs to be two-way traffic by the way – there may be some things they need to tell you, too!

"Hmm? Oh yeah, big boy ... I'm nearly there."

Don't stop me now

A mistake men often make is to stop stimulating us at the critical moment. When a woman is about to come, it's really important to keep on doing exactly the same thing to her clitoris that's brought her to that point – whether it's with your fingers, tongue, or a vibrator. Changing your rhythm or stroke at the eleventh hour can throw us off course – and unfortunately we don't share the same 'orgasmic inevitability' as you!

This tip also goes for girls stimulating guys – although most men do seem to like the action speeded up a little just before they climax and then slowed right down, or stopped, as they ejaculate.

Women are different – sometimes we like it if you *continue* stimulation – very gently – through our orgasmic spasms (and there can be between 3 and 15 of these, gradually subsiding in intensity). Sometimes we might just like a hand cupped gently over our vulvas as we float down from the ceiling. Or then again, maybe we'd like your hand filling the kettle for a cuppa. The bottom line is we'll only know what's best if we ask each other and learn to read each other's signals.

Thanks for the mammaries

Human females are the only mammals with breasts that jut out when we're not pregnant or breastfeeding – and *boy, don't we know it*. Fortunately, they're a major erogenous zone for many women – some can even orgasm through nipple stimulation alone, and most enjoy everything from gentle sucking to firm tweaking. Men enjoy nipple play too – try pinching theirs quite hard, or apply heated lube to nipples and blow for an extra buzz ...

"Mmmmmmmmmmm ... no, don't stop NOW!"

Holby clitty

In the late 19th and early 20th Centuries, it was deemed entirely normal for doctors to stimulate their female patients to orgasm. Sometimes a midwife would assist, but it was mostly well-paid male physicians who aroused ladies to 'paroxysms' in order to relieve their 'hysteria'. So that's what they mean by a good bedside manner ...

Going with the flow

Female ejaculation is not a myth. It may only be about 10% of women who have the ability to do it – and the jury is still out about exactly what the fluid is – but it certainly isn't an embarrassing display of orgasm-induced incontinence. Clinical analysis has revealed that although it's expelled from the urethra (so it can sometimes smell a little like urine) it is in fact the female equivalent of prostatic fluid. So it's similar to male ejaculate – slippery in consistency, but only slightly milky in colour, and obviously minus the sperm content!

On page 22, *Elusive but effusive*, I've given details about how to locate your G-spot – considered to generate the type of orgasm that produces female ejaculate. (You can of course have a G-spot orgasm and not ejaculate.) When the spot is first touched it can be uncomfortable, because you will feel the need to pee, even if you've already emptied your bladder. You won't wet the bed I promise, but for peace of mind you might want to conduct any initial explorations with a towel underneath you. The urge to go to the loo will soon be replaced by a deeply satisfying sensation if you continue stimulation.

It helps to be feeling as turned on as possible, as the G-spot swells when it's aroused. It responds well to firm pressure, so stroke it gently (but like you mean business) with a circular, or a 'come here' beckoning motion. Better still, get your lover to do the massaging, especially if they can go down on you at the same time. Alternatively, stimulate your clitoris manually whilst using a vibrator specifically designed for G-spot massage – a good one is Sensual Essentials' waterproof Little Paul which will guarantee the consistent pressure you need.

If you're making love, the best positions are doggy-style and woman on top. It can be trial and error getting the exact angle for his penis to induce your orgasm – and smaller members are actually better for the purpose. (Told you big isn't always best.)

A G-spot climax can take some time to achieve, but it's worth the wait – it's an extreme, dramatic, limb-tingling experience – whether you ejaculate or not. And if you bear down, pushing your PC muscles out rather than clenching them in, just as you're about to come, then you'll increase your chances of squirting or gushing – and amazing your significant other. Congratulations! That towel might come in handy after all ...

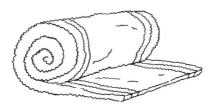

chapter 5
Going it alone

The word masturbation is derived from the Latin 'manu stuprare', meaning to 'defile with the hand', and up until quite recently the dictionary definition was 'self-abuse'. Back in the 1880s, castration was even performed to remedy this appalling habit, and numerous devices were invented to deter and punish its evil practitioners.

Thankfully we no longer subscribe to the Victorian belief that pleasuring ourselves leads to blindness, madness, genital deformities, and nose bleeds (but it is still true, of course, that it causes enormous clumps of black hair to sprout from the palms of our hands).

Hey – get over it. It's a small price to pay for something that feels so great. The official party line today is buy some depilatory cream and keep taking yourself in hand – *masturbation is good for you*. It's the most widely practised method of safe sex, you don't have to worry about anyone else, and you don't even have to shave your legs – or your palms ... (only kidding by the way).

Seriously, it's not just about pleasure, you're in training – to be a more skilled, aware, and responsive lover. If you're an expert at making yourself climax, you'll have increased desire (the more sex you have, the more you want) and the knowledge to teach your partner what you like best. You're taking responsibility for your sexual happiness – plus it doesn't half help you get off to sleep.

Let's not forget Woody Allen's wise words on flying solo – "Don't knock masturbation. It's sex with someone I love." Good on you, Woody. I bet he's got *really* hairy palms ...

Coming into view

Both men and women often complain that partners don't touch them the way they would like to be touched. So masturbate in front of each other if you dare – it takes courage, but it's worth it. You may feel a little embarrassed at first, but what better way of showing each other what you like best, by letting someone witness first-hand how you touch yourself. Not to mention that the sight of you open – in every sense – and losing yourself in your own (normally private) ecstasy is an incredible turn-on in its own right.

Cereal chiller

In 1894, Dr. John Harvey Kellogg, an obsessive celibate, invented an anti-masturbatory food designed to take away all sexual desire – the product was called Cornflakes. It's certainly not one of the benefits listed on the packet today, and thankfully no one subscribes to his other dubious theories either. For little boys, Dr. Kellogg advocated circumcision without anaesthetic or 'covering the organs with a cage', whereas for females he advised 'the application of pure carbolic acid to the clitoris' for the purpose of 'allaying the abnormal excitement'. Ouch.

Sole sensation

This works for both sexes. Try putting the soles of your feet together when you masturbate, so your knees are splayed out to the side. It increases pressure in the groin, making everything even more enjoyable and intensifying your climax.

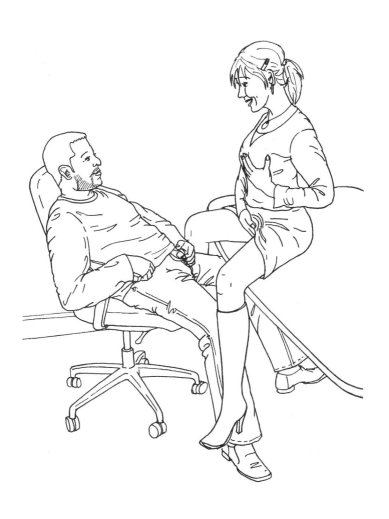

Fastest finger first

Let him catch you pleasuring yourself, girls – and having a very nice time. You've carefully orchestrated matters of course, so he 'accidentally' finds you moaning and writhing in ecstasy – and the trick is to be so carried away that you can't stop (i.e. you're a wild, shameless hussy). Bet you any money that once he gets used to the idea, he'll be desperate to join in the fun.

Greased lightning

If you've never tried masturbating with lube before, you guys are in for one mega-treat. Any specialist lubricant will do, but for the best sensations, splash out and invest in an oil-based cream. They're made specifically for male masturbation, and they're not recommended for vaginas – so she won't try to steal it (like you do with her moisturiser ... ?).

They're also extremely long-lasting – they don't dry out, even if you pump away for hours (as you may well want to when you discover it). Take a look at ID Masturbation Cream – one user reports, "Second only to the real thing – and sometimes even better." Thanks a bunch!

It's for you

Hot and horny and stuck at work? Turn off your mailbox setting, put your mobile on vibrate, pop it in your knickers and ring it ... lots.

Minge benefits

Shop for some of the less expensive briefs with gussets that aren't sewn down – they make convenient 'envelopes' for slipping phones or compact vibrators into.

Centre spread

Place your forefinger and your middle finger at the top of your outer labia – on either side, so they're in a downward 'V' shape. Then pull them upwards to stretch your inner labia and expose your clitoris – not just for easier access, but because it creates a liberating feeling of being 'opened up'. Keep them there as you masturbate with your other hand, and try this when your lover touches you too. Alternatively, some women prefer the feeling of pressing down just above the bikini line – have a play and see which you prefer. Either way, if you're struggling to come, but just can't seem to get there, giving yourself a helping hand can tip you over the edge.

Wank-a-thon

Europe's first sponsored Masturbate-a-thon was held on August 5th, 2006 in London. Commissioned by Channel 4 in the UK as part of a series of programmes called 'Wank Week', it was also known as the Wank-a-thon. Participants were expected "to masturbate in order to raise money for charity and dispel the shame and taboos that persist around this form of sexual activity".

If you'd like to raise money for good causes but you don't fancy playing with yourself in public, the month of May has now been designated Masturbation Month. So you can pleasure yourself at home to your heart's content – and get everyone to sponsor you into the bargain! Money for old grope ...

"I don't know how they can do it in that position
– it's just so degrading for the woman."

chapter 6
Take your places

The original erotic self-help manual, the *Kama Sutra*, may be centuries old, but we're still using spin-offs of the 64 positions it teaches – we just don't do the ones that require circus skills to execute, and we tend to give them other names now. (Shame really, a spot of 'suspended congress' sounds rather intriguing.)

I reckon that in reality there are about a dozen basic ways of having nooky that are do-able without making us dissolve into fits of giggles, or feel like we're playing Twister. Here are a few that I think really work – if any are not in your current repertoire and you fancy giving them a go, try them a few times. The first attempt may seem a bit mechanical, but second and third time around you can begin to make them your own, creating your own variations, and things should start to fall into place.

Say it again Sam

With any position, or foreplay, try complementing the action with dirty dialogue – a sort of 'running commentary' on what you're doing – or all the wicked, depraved things you're going to do – if you think that might be well received. Talking during sex can make things über-erotic, especially if you're normally silent. You don't have to use swear words or be a genius with your sentence construction – just start small and whisper dirty nothings in each other's ears. Do it a lot, and certain words or phrases can easily become a 'trigger' that not only speeds arousal, but orgasm too.

Dolphins

The man lies on his back with his legs slightly apart. His partner lies on top facing him, with his penis in her and her legs together and straight, between his. She pushes up on her hands, as if doing a press-up, supporting her upper body weight. This way she's able to grind her clitoris against his pubic bone as she slides forward and back on him. Circular gyrating movements work too – or a combination of both.

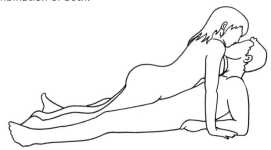

Another variation is to have her legs apart and his together, between hers. Either way the trick is for the woman to use her pubic bone as a kind of pivot – she's in charge and therefore able to give herself maximum stimulation, with the potential for both clitoral and G-spot orgasms.

A fringe benefit for the guy is that he doesn't have much work to do, and a huge fringe benefit for her is that she can rest her body on his, which is a perfect position for those deep, meaningful kisses I banged on about in *Chapter 1*. After which, you can gaze lovingly into each other's eyes ... what do you mean I'm soppy?

Count to 10

This one is good for releasing the animal within you both, but as with all doggy-style positions, vaginal penetration is deep, so if you're well-endowed, you're best to start gently and build up to more energetic thrusting.

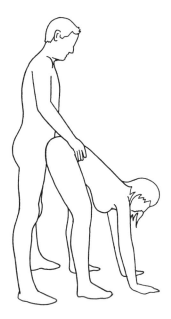

The woman bends forward from the waist, feet apart, knees bent, and with her hands resting flat on the ground. The man stands behind her (she drew the short straw). He then takes hold of her hips and slowly penetrates her, affirming his alpha male status. She is exposed and submissive, whilst Tarzan is totally in control – and enjoying the view. This is a great posture for G-spot stimulation, as his penis is perfectly positioned to hit her hot-spot, and for variety she can move her hands up onto her knees or brace herself against a wall, chair, tree, or whatever offers stable support.

The *Kama Sutra* calls this the 'congress of a cow' and advises that 'the characteristics of these animals should be manifested by acting like them'. Hmm.

I call it 'Count to 10' because with such a visual feast – plus the possibility of fondling your swinging breasts – it's all going to be over in seconds. Moooo ... .

Yawning yoni

This is useful if she's feeling fairly wild and abandoned, and up for showing off her yoni. He gets the erotic thrill of seeing her spread open, plus the added excitement of watching himself disappearing in and out of her wetness. He also gets to drill deep – so it's a good position for smaller penises, as it gives her a more 'full up' feeling.

The woman lies on her back and raises her knees towards her chest. He kneels up against her bottom with his legs parted, and penetrates her, with his hands on her thighs. She can rest her feet against his chest, or on his shoulders, but the closer she draws her knees to her chest, the deeper he'll go, and the bigger he'll feel inside her.

Please note – the higher her legs, the more the stomach is scrunched up and likely to wobble. If she's been overdoing the

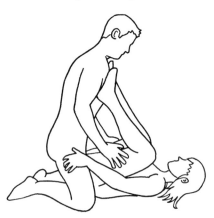

crisps/wine/Curly Wurlys, then she might feel it necessary to cover her tummy with her hands to hide the evidence. A clever move that not only disguises her innate lack of discipline, but also allows her to press down just above her pubic bone to enhance stimulation. Known in the trade as the Yoni bone-us.

Sensual spoons

This is a relaxing, comfortable classic, and a favourite for many. Great for lazy sex, oh-go-on-then-if-you-have-to sex, sleepy middle of the night sex, or when the woman is pregnant.

She lies on her side, and the man lies on his side behind her – echoing her position, and holding her close. He can stimulate her clitoris, massage her breasts, and cover her neck with kisses – and she can just relish the attention.

To make access to her clitoris easier, she can wrap her uppermost leg back over her partners, and pleasure herself – manually or with a vibrator. She can then return his favours by reaching through her legs and stroking his balls – again with her fingers or a vibe.

For a new spin on spoons, try matching your breathing to your partner's, so you're totally in rhythm with each other. Synchronising your breathing, so you're inhaling and exhaling simultaneously – especially through orgasm – can make you closer spiritually, and bring a new intimacy and understanding to your lovemaking.

chapter 7
Tease & please

Recent statistics state that most women require around 20 minutes to achieve orgasm, which is pretty imbalanced when the average man can achieve his in around two. No matter what our differences, foreplay is the warm-up that works for us all – with benefits reaching far beyond the bedroom. Couples flirt more, they feel cared for, they're better able to tune into what turns each other on – and not just between the sheets.

Be creative with your foreplay. Vary the pace, vary the place. Try warming up in the woods, or some teasing as you watch TV. Begin with a slow sensual massage, or wash each other's hair. Cuddle up and watch some porn (you won't stay at the cuddling stage for long), or read erotic fiction out loud to each other (try Nancy Friday, or Scarlet magazine has an extremely steamy section called 'Cliterature'). You could even make up your own.

There are hundreds of ways to spice up your sex life, it's all about deciding to – focussing in on each other, and letting your imaginations run wild. Read on for some more raunchy ideas – it's foreplay Jim, but maybe not as we know it ...

You can leave your hat on

Actually never mind your hat – keep your panties on though. Whether they're delicate lacy ones, big white schoolgirl pants or a difference-splitting thong, there's something reminiscent of teenage fumblings that makes this incredibly sexy for you both, not to mention the bonus of added friction. And don't just insist on wearing them during foreplay – yank that moist gusset aside for penetration too.

Ring the changes

Variety, said to be the spice of life, can also spice up your sex life. Surprise your partner by daring to be different. If your usual style is soft and gentle, try playing a bit harder and dominating things. Or if your lovemaking is normally more animal, try taking your time with a slow, sensual approach. Don't get into a rut with foreplay either – turn things around; if you generally start with kissing on the mouth, head straight into kissing down south. Just one departure from your usual routine can reap exciting dividends.

Don't dress for dinner

It produces a rather interesting effect if you go out for a meal and 'forget' to dress. This is obviously best carried out when temperatures are mild, and in the kind of restaurant where it won't look too strange for a girl to keep her mac on. When your partner realises the only thing between them and you is your coat, killer heels and maybe some sexy stockings, there's a strong chance you might not make it to dessert.

Be prepared

Dangerous quickies that carry with them the adrenalin-rush of being caught, are wonderful for adding some heart-pounding thrills to your usual repertoire. Just remember it is illegal to have sex in public, so if you're going to have an alfresco quickie somewhere you shouldn't, think about ways to disguise matters – or a feasible story you can tell if an authority figure rumbles you. "She had something stuck in her throat, officer, and I was dislodging it with this tool" might not totally convince.

"… and Sir, I believe you ordered the muffin."

Great sextextations

When I first heard this tip I wasn't very impressed, but I can now say first hand it works – 100%. Send a seriously dirty text (and I'm talking X-rated) to your loved one, and then wait for their shocked reply! It's so unexpected to read hard-core personal porn on your mobile, rather than 'Will be at station in 5 mins' that it really raises the game, and makes you both feel like you're newly together and in lust all over again ...

Wet 'n' wild

The next time your partner is taking a shower, surprise them by joining in – with your clothes on. Actions that abandon practicality in favour of passion can lift you both out of your comfort zone and be an enormous turn-on.

Sex and the Civic

Having sex in a car is not for the fainthearted or the romantic, but it's a surprisingly popular pursuit in the UK. In fact 50% of adults in the latest Durex global survey, said it was their favourite location outside of the bedroom. If a stretch limo just happens to be at your disposal all well and good, but for most it's a choice of his Honda Civic or her Ford Fiesta. So if you're planning to make out in a motor there are three simple rules to observe, to save you steering feet first down Cringe Street.

1. **Stop!** Check you've not got company (unless you're into dogging and you get off on having an audience). And it's not a great idea to perform a sexual act whilst your partner is actually driving.

2. **Look!** Be careful to get rid of any incriminating evidence after in-car copulation has occurred (especially if the car's not your own.) Clean up any footprints on the windscreen if you were bracing your feet against it, and remember to check for used condoms in the ash-tray.

3. **Listen!** Opt for the passenger side or the back seat – in preference to the driver's side – when doing the deed itself. A well-upholstered bottom can inadvertently make contact with the car's horn, which may be a slight giveaway and is guaranteed to cramp your style. You'll be laughing enough as it is.

"How much is it to send these first class?"

Panties by post

If you're working away from home and your partner is missing you between the sheets, give them a treat with an aromatic reminder of you. Package up a pair of your freshly-worn panties and post them (just make sure they go First Class!). For express delivery, with an added conspiratorial thrill, send them gift-wrapped via a work colleague. This one's not just for the girls either – both sexes love the fresh musk of their partner, and it's a different way to say "Wish you were here ... "

You can ring my bell

Telephone sex can be a powerful aphrodisiac – or a good way of keeping things fuelled if you're parted from your loved one and can only communicate by phone. Speak softly and start slowly by describing to each other what you're wearing, and how you wish he could see you in your skimpy negligee, or how the mere thought of her is making you bulge obscenely, etc. Then build the tension by telling each other what you're doing – and don't spare the details – in fact the more intimate and explicit you dare to be, the greater the turn-on for your lucky listener.

Best of all is that unless you're on a video phone, you can be nestled up in your winceyette jim-jams/not-so-nice Y-fronts, and no one's any the wiser – just allow your imagination to run riot and let your fingers do the walking ...

Sacrificial lingerie

There's something wild and wonderful about tearing each other's clothes off – and I'm talking literally. I once had a memorably lustful exchange with a boyfriend who burst in on me in a theatre dressing room, and ripped open the tight Victorian bodice that was part of my costume. As the twenty-odd tiny fastenings pinged across the room, I did for a nano-second think what a pain in the arse it was going to be sewing them all back on, but this was soon blitzed by the heady euphoria induced by his wanton, button-popping desire.

That was an unexpected and spontaneous moment, but there's no reason why you can't *plan* a bodice-ripping scenario. From a practical point of view it's best if buttons and seams are quite loose, so you could use old clothes or lingerie that's on its last legs (which is obviously the most economical if you were already thinking of chucking them).

On the other hand, if you feel your tatty old smalls just don't have what it takes anymore, then invest in new stuff, though you may need to loosen some fixings or stitching so it splits apart more easily. Of course it makes it sexier the more gorgeous you look, but maybe consider undies that are a bit cheaper and flimsier than you'd normally wear – there's no point in buying quality, because it's all going to get torn to shreds in the throes of passion anyway. That red nylon G-string you got for Christmas may come in handy after all ...

Little white lie

Take an insider tip from Hollywood heart-throb Cary Grant
"To succeed with the opposite sex, tell her you're impotent. She can't wait to disprove it."

Meat and greet

Prepare supper starkers – or wearing only a fetching little apron to protect you from hot splashes. Hopefully the sight of you in the buff will produce lots of those anyway, but you'll probably have removed your pinny by then. Men look especially good in those long, stripey, serious chef numbers, with just their bare bums on show ... nice.

"Sorry, she can't come to the phone right now – she's having lunch."

chapter 8
A taste of things to come

If you want to shine on the sensual stage, it seems there's no better way to win accolades than by being a cunnilingus or fellatio star. A magic tongue will win you a standing ovation every time, so read on for some top oral tips:

For her

1. First and foremost, learn to really love giving him head (or do the finest acting job you're capable of). You'll have no happier audience than your man as he listens to your appreciative groans while you gobble him. Don't be afraid to be a noisy eater.

2. It's not a lollypop, so don't just lick his penis. Always involve your hands, by sliding one fist up and down the shaft, with a consistent rhythm that begins slowly and builds gradually. Use a confident but comfortable stroke – experiment with several variations – whilst sucking him gently at the same time. Keep your lips covering your teeth and remember the head is super-sensitive. Use your other hand to press firmly up against his perineum to massage his prostate from the outside.

3. He needs your mouth, and hand, to be as wet as possible. If your saliva isn't too forthcoming, increase its flow – and his pleasure – by using a flavoured lubricant. The juicier the better.

4. For an extra visual thrill try going down on your knees – it's a subservient pose many men love. If your hair is long try tying it back to give him a better view, and put the spotlight on your skills by leaving the lights on.

For him

1. Make her believe you've got all the time in the world, and you want her to take at *least* an hour to come. Women are much slower than men, and if we think you're bored or tired we'll never get there. Ease any pressure, and we'll be beating a path to your door.

2. Take our cue and go very slowly yourself – most women don't enjoy fast and furious, especially at first. Use masses of saliva, licking everywhere else before our clits (to drive us mad with desire) and stimulating us with lazy, flat-tongued licks – pointing your tongue can be too intense (and tiring for you). Get her to show you how she'd like it, by demonstrating her favourite strokes on your palm.

3. Tell her she has the most beautiful vulva and it's driving you crazy seeing her wide open. It doesn't matter if it's true or not – the confidence will make her blossom. Whisper that her smell and taste is really sexy – we're all worried about our girly bits, and a little reassurance goes a long way.

4. If we've swallowed, and we come back up for a kiss, please can you actually give us one?! Many men seem revolted by the idea that they might actually taste some semen. What's the big problem? It's sexy – and it is yours, after all!

What's in it for me?

Semen contains only 5 to 15 calories per ejaculation, a protein content similar to the white of a large egg, and about 60% of the American recommended daily intake for vitamin C – beats Haliborange any day.

"It contains nyacin, loads of vitamin C …
and best of all, it's low calorie and low fat!"

Blow-job eyes

You might feel like you're in a porn movie, but choose a moment to look up at him when you're going down. Holding eye contact a little too long is always a powerful trick to signal desire, and making blow-job eyes when you're between his legs is a clear signal that you enjoy giving, as well as receiving, a little lip service.

The top five things to have in your mouth (as well as each other)

1. **An ice cube** – if you find this difficult, try freezing some grapes or berries – much tastier too. Alternate with bursts of stimulation from a hot (but not boiling) drink to electrify nerve endings.

2. **Champagne** – the bubbles also stimulate nerve endings, increasing skin sensitivity. This isn't the easiest of techniques to master, but sparkling mineral water makes a good cheap alternative until you get the hang of it!

3. **A mint** – the stronger the better – delivers a fascinating hot/cold sensation that lingers on even after the action has stopped. Peppermint generally favoured over Spearmint – or try toothpaste.

4. **Sherbet** – or anything containing it – explodes in your mouth (as will the recipient).

5. **A tongue piercing** – *only* if carried out by a reputable specialist. Not for the faint-hearted, but if it appeals to you, your oral won't be ordinary. Try freezing tongue jewellery first, then drink hot tea – same effect as an ice cube/hot drink but even more pronounced.

Stubble trouble

I'm all for a sexy two-day growth, but it hurts like hell when it's in direct contact with the delicate female vulva (the words *sand* and *paper* spring to mind). We love you going down there guys – we just don't want our labia to feel like they've been rubbed back ready for primer and undercoat. Scheduling in a shave earns you major brownie points, but if you're deeply attached to your designer stubble or you sport the full Captain Birdseye, you might like to consider smoothing some hair conditioner on your whiskers prior to heading south. Leave it on for a few minutes beforehand and we'll be saying 'Aye aye, Cap'n' before you know it.

The sweet taste of success

If you'd like your partner to swallow, but they don't like the taste, try sweetening your seed by eating strawberries, melon or kiwi fruit, sprinkled with cinnamon. Drinking lots of cranberry or pineapple juice can help too (pineapple is also used in the homeopathic cure for impotence). You should reduce your intake of curry, cigarettes, coffee, alcohol, salt, and garlic – as these make semen taste bitter and briny, whilst asparagus and dairy products won't do you any favours at all. For a supremely tasty load, try wheatgrass juice – not cheap, but an investment worth making!

Eliminating red-eye

You don't have to swallow if you don't want to (in fact it's definitely advisable *not* to if you don't know your partner's sexual history – so use a flavoured condom, then you don't even have the problem). It is however, considered rude and insulting to spit semen out with a horrified grimace, so try having him ejaculate on your body as an erotic alternative. Shooting over your neck and breasts gives you a 'pearl necklace' to massage in, but if he aims higher, then be careful of 'a shot in the eye' – it stings big-time and causes redness for hours.

Last night of the hums

Oh alright – you don't actually have to sing *Land of Hope and Glory* when you're feasting on each other, but humming gives both sexes fascinating sensations in the nether regions. The deeper the hum, the more powerful the vibration, and you won't feel quite so daft if you make a sort of "mmm" sound as you suck, as in "mmm this is nice" – which of course it is ...

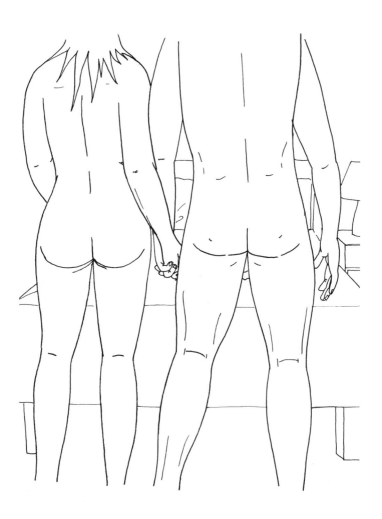

chapter 9
Rear view

The anus has the highest concentration of erotically sensitive nerve endings next to our genitals, and providing you're both in agreement, a foray into some rear action can give intense pleasure, as well as establishing a new level of intimacy. Anal play still carries a taboo tag, but its illicit 'dirtiness' only adds to the thrill. It's now becoming much more mainstream for both sexes, whatever your sexual orientation.

There's a saying that women try anal sex twice — once to see what it's like, and the second time to see if it really was that bad. Witty, but fortunately not accurate. In reality, women get off on the feeling of fullness — in both the anus and vagina, as they share a 'party wall'. And men not only love the tightness of their partner's anal canal, but they're also awakening to the fact that they can enjoy being on the receiving end of anal play — and it doesn't mean they're gay — just enlightened and in touch with their bodies. (Incidentally, the majority of gay men report that oral is their number one sexual activity.)

Remember that our anal sphincter muscles are well practised at pushing things out, rather than taking things in. We're conditioned from infancy to grip them closed, so when anything is about to invade our bottoms, our response isn't usually 'Dive right in baby, the water's fine'. It requires both a physical and a psychological shift to relax and allow something through, where it's normally one-way traffic. Give your sphincter — and your head — space to adjust.

A bum steer

Some chaps would rather consume a close relative than have you venture into their forbidden territory. Equally, it drives the fairer sex bonkers when men play 'How did I get the wrong hole?', as they attempt to shove their huge, throbbing, *unlubricated* members into our sweet, innocent, *unlubricated* rosebuds. Do both parties a favour, by first trying to gauge if the other one actually fancies the idea, but if that's not possible you can usually tell if they're keen by reading their body language.

If you're close to their backdoor, and your partner arches their back and pushes – or wiggles – their bottom towards you (think monkeys in the zoo) then you're probably heading in the right direction. (On second thoughts, perhaps don't think monkeys.) If they jump out of their skins and yell, chances are your anal advances may not be so welcome. Talk it through first, *always* issue a warning of what your partner is about to receive – *and keep things lubricated!*

Cardinal rules

Immaculate hygiene is a must, so bathe, shower, or use a bidet before embarking up the bum, and always wash hands and organs thoroughly after use. Fingernails should be very short and smooth – the skin inside the rectum tears easily and long nails can damage this fragile area.

Take everything *very slowly* if it's new territory for you. You can avoid pain if you use masses of good lubrication, massage around the area first, and really take your time to allow the sphincter muscles to adapt and relax – give each other progress reports as you go. Remember that the anal area has no natural lubrication, so it's absolutely essential to use a thick, gooey, silicone- or water-based lube – both latex-friendly for condoms – and to reapply it frequently. This will guard against damaging delicate anal tissue and lessen the possibility of condoms splitting. Besides which, it hurts like hell if you don't – and that's guaranteed to put you off instantly.

The bottom line

It's crucial with anal play to observe a strict safety code and to be extremely gentle. Never let yourself be forced into trying it if you don't want to. Remember though, that anal doesn't have to involve intercourse – the biggest concentration of nerve endings is around the opening itself, making it very responsive to both manual and oral stimulation, so you may just want to try a starter without necessarily moving on to the main course! It's also better if you're feeling seriously horny, as this will help you to relax and be receptive – in every sense.

Ring-a-ring a rosebud …

Get relaxed and aroused by massaging your partner's derrière first – spreading their cheeks, then softly squeezing them, and moving them round in circles. Next start gently stimulating the outside of the anus, again in a circular motion, with a well-lubricated finger. Slowly slide your finger a little way in, and if your partner is comfortable and likes the sensation, go a little deeper, still keeping a circular, rather than an in-out motion, to get the anus used to being stretched in this way. You can try inserting a second finger (constantly checking if it's OK to do so) and then slide them gently in and out, but don't withdraw your finger(s) completely, as this is what tends to cause discomfort.

Up at the crack

You can also experiment with "rimming", which is using your tongue to explore each other anally, also called analingus. Begin by building anticipation, with long teasing licks up from the perineum first. This is the fleshy area between the anus and testicles in men, and the anus and vagina in women, and it's a potential erotic hotbed in its own right.

Some people may like stimulation to stop at the perineum, but if appreciative moans are giving you the signal to continue, then make your tongue as stiff as possible to give the most pleasurable sensations. If you're a bit squeamish, or worried about infection, try using a dental dam or a piece of cling-film. If you don't have either to hand, cut open a flavoured condom and use that instead.

SURGICAL

HOUSEHOLD

INDUSTRIAL

Manicure-cure

You might adore your beautiful lengthy talons, but your partner's anus won't. Long or ragged nails can do some serious damage to the delicate anal tissues, but if you can't bear to give them the chop, then wear a pair of latex gloves – you can even buy them in black (not just sexy, but practical too). They'll make all anal play safe and smooth, and by popping some cotton wool under your nails before putting them on you'll lessen the chances of them piercing the latex – or anything else. (And if your partner is into rubber or latex, a gloved hand job will have them squirming with pleasure.)

Reach out and touch

You can spice up the missionary position by reaching round and inserting a well-lubricated finger into your man as he thrusts, providing he's up for it – and your arms are long enough! This can be intensely stimulating for him as his orgasm is approaching, and keeping it there will really enhance his climax.

Prostate milking

Prostate milking refers to the centuries old practice of relieving the build-up of semen by prostate massage. You can still drive him wild by stimulating his P-spot, more commonly known as the prostate gland, and considered to be the male equivalent of the female G-Spot.

Slowly penetrate him as far as you can, with your longest lubed-up finger – his anus should be lubricated as well. You should be able to locate a small, firm bump on the uppermost side of his anal passage, in the direction of his navel, which has a slightly crinkly texture like a walnut. Press, or stroke this P-spot with a rhythmic, beckoning motion (just like for the female G-spot) but be gentle – and make sure it's your finger pad and not your nail, that's making contact.

Some men can be milked to orgasm solely through prostate stimulation. If his penis is waving around and crying out for attention though, suck or stroke it with your other hand to bring him to a powerful, knee-trembling climax, and withdraw your finger very s-l-o-w-l-y when it's all over. (See also *The second coming*, page 44).

Delve a little deeper

If you're ready to try anal intercourse, then doggy-style or spoons is easiest for newbies, followed by missionary, with knees pulled up to the chest. Straddling him on top means you're in control – which is good – but it does tend to tighten the anal muscles, so penetration is more difficult. Don't forget to stimulate your clitoris to relax and arouse yourself – the more turned-on you are, the easier it will be. Use your hand or a vibrator if that's better for you.

Making sure you're both greased to the hilt, ask him to slowly massage your anus with his penis. If you then push out – as if you're trying to have a bowel movement – that will help to relax the outer sphincter and you can lower yourself back onto his penis – there's no thrusting at this stage. Breathe deeply, and once the head is in, leave it there. Stop and relax for as long as you need to get used to the sensation – the one who's being penetrated calls the shots here, so you set the pace. When you're ready, ease more of him in, oh-sooo slowly, and then relax again. If you're comfortable, he can then do some shallow thrusting, but make sure you're in constant communication so he knows immediately if you're not OK.

Don't worry if you don't manage full insertion at first – you might need a few goes to get the hang of it. It's much more important to be safe, to take your time, and to build up trust between you.

Blowin' in the wind

There's no getting away from it – anal sex can involve wind. If air goes in (as it can with the thrusting motion) it's going to need to come out – another reason to embark on it only with someone you trust and really feel at ease with. You need to know that a fart, if it happens, isn't going to make either of you curl up in paroxysms of embarrassment. It helps, if you're on the receiving end, to go to the loo as soon as you can afterwards, and maybe turn the volume up on the radio, if you're worried about any noisy after-effects!

Getting in shape

Butt plugs can be useful to train the anal passage and enable either of you to enjoy the feeling of fullness they provide. (They can also be used during masturbation or to enhance conventional intercourse.) Available in various sizes and materials, they should always be scrutinised for rough edges, as any object for insertion must be smooth to be safe. They're designed to be eased in, then left in place for the session, so make sure they *always* have a T-bar or flared end, to prevent the very real risk of them being 'swallowed up' – the sphincter muscles are surprisingly powerful. Start small if you're a beginner so you don't feel overwhelmed, and use tons of lube – both on the plug and on yourself.

"Can you remember what ring size you are darling?"

The bum's rush

Never ever make a quick exit from a bottom – with fingers
or a penis – pull out as slowly and carefully as you went in.
The sphincter muscles (and there's a double set of them) will
involuntarily contract and tense up if you rush things, and neither
you, nor your steamy sex session, will have a happy ending.

Open sesame (or maybe not)

This may sound a bit gross, but let's be practical here. If you're
planning being on the receiving end of some anal activity in
the near future, make sure you get enough roughage in your
diet to keep your bowels healthy and clear, but avoid sweetcorn
or foods containing lots of seeds, as these tend to remain whole
and sometimes overstay their welcome.

Dump the anxiety

A lot of people think that just inside the entrance to your
bottom lives a whole load of poo, sitting ready and waiting.
Wrong. Faeces is manufactured much higher up in the colon –
the rectum and anal canal are only passageways, so if our habits
are regular, they're usually clear. It obviously makes sense to go
to the loo before you begin, and thoroughly wash and/or use
unscented wipes to keep clean, but venturing where the sun
don't shine is a lot less messy than you'd imagine.

Some final anal rules

1. *Always* wear a condom (with the possible exception of monogamous couples who've been fluid-bonded for decades). Anal play is the riskiest transmission route for HIV and other sexually transmitted infections, so penises should always be latex-clad. Pop them on anal toys too – for safety and to make cleaning up easier.

2. Never *ever* transfer a finger, a penis, or a toy, from an anus to a vagina without washing it first. They might do it in porn movies, and you might think you'll lose spontaneity if you stop and wash, but your safety is paramount here. No matter how clean your bottom is, anal bacteria can cause nasty infections in the vagina, so don't cross-pollinate.

3. Never use numbing creams for anal sex. Don't disguise any discomfort – anal sex is only painful if it's not done correctly, so pain is an important warning signal from our bodies that we ought to be aware of.

4. You can never have too much lube for anal. Take a generous amount – then double it.

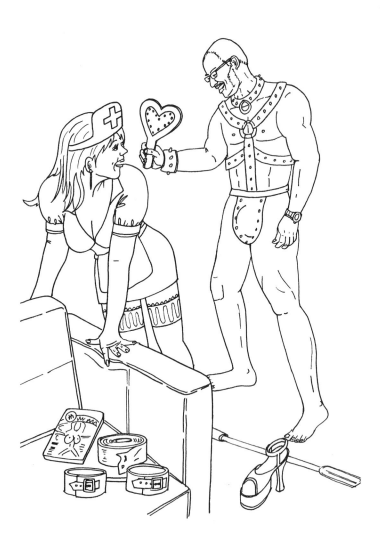

chapter 10
Fantasies & fetishes

The biggest erogenous zone we possess is between our ears. The brain is our most potent erotic organ, and plays a central role in our sexual arousal. Indulging in dark, forbidden daydreams can supercharge our sensuality and prove an invaluable tool for both masturbation and lovemaking.

It's up to us how mad, bad and dangerous we get – fantasies are about exploring our kinkiest thoughts. There are no rules and regulations, so we shouldn't hold back or be ashamed of our innermost desires – or be disturbed by them. By having wild, illicit role-plays in our heads, we get to imagine all kinds of sleazy scenarios that we wouldn't remotely consider acting out in real life (well OK, maybe the one about Brad Pitt if you insist).

It's fine to keep a fantasy private, but if we step out of our comfort zone and dare to share, it can revolutionise a relationship, bringing greater intimacy and new sexual highs. Pick your moment carefully, and sensitively gauge your significant other's reaction – suddenly announcing your secret yearning can sometimes be threatening, especially if they wonder why you didn't trust them enough to let on before.

Pretending you had an erotic dream is often a good way of revealing a fantasy, and might encourage an exchange of secrets, or maybe some experimental role-playing – if you're both up for it. Don't assume that just because they love us, our partners instinctively know what we want – and never make fun of each other's revelations. We need to come clean – and then we can come dirty.

Quality control

Just like emails on a computer, our mental store of sexual fantasies can get clogged up and stale if we don't do some housekeeping from time to time. Of course, we might have some fantasies that are cherished and special to us, that we need to save for easy access and a shortcut to fulfilment. There are probably some old chestnuts, though, that came to us years ago but just don't cut the mustard any more. Re-examine your Inbox and start clearing – to make room for new material that packs a more powerful erotic punch for who you are now.

Colette's tip

If your partner fancies someone else, try not to be threatened by their admission. Why not bring the third party to bed with you instead? I don't mean literally (unless of course you've all agreed this is an avenue you want to go down, and could handle the consequences). I mean *talk* in bed with your partner about the person they fancy, what they'd like to do with them, maybe invent a fantasy together around them that could even involve the three of you. It might be Robbie Williams or the girl next door, but it can become your shared secret, and instead of you feeling insecure, you're taking charge – and it can bring you closer together.

"And tonight, babe, I am going to be …"

Her top three fantasies

1. Being overpowered, restrained and taken by force.
2. Sex with another woman.
3. Being a dominatrix – with him as the sex slave.

His top three fantasies

1. Sex with his woman (ahhh).
2. Sex with two or more women
   (dressed as nurses/hookers/maids ...)
3. Being tied and trussed up – then 'feasted' on.

Bondage for beginners

Experiment with bondage by starting with tights or a silk
scarf to tie up your partner – whatever's accessible and not too
threatening. Avoid pressure points, and never leave someone when
they're tied up – or have them tied for longer than half an hour.
If any body part goes cold or purple it's a warning sign, so undo
all knots *immediately*. In fact it's a good idea to have some
scissors standing by if you weren't in the Scouts or Guides!

Restraining orders

If you'd like to go a little further with the ties that bind, you can
buy a 2 inch (5 cm) wide custom-made tape that sticks to itself
without adhesive. Available in black and several other colours,
it forms a secure bond but is painlessly removed – even from
hair. It can also be used to create sexy outfits and any part of the
body can be gift-wrapped. If you've ever fancied playing 'pass the
parcel' with you in the starring role – now's your opportunity ...

Rules of the game

Only play sex games with someone you instinctively trust, and never with someone you've only just met. Spend some time getting to know each other first, and take it from there – if you feel you'd like to.

Keeping the code

With any BDSM (Bondage, Domination, Sado-Masochism) activity, or other practices that carry a degree of danger, first decide on a safety or emergency word or phrase, which you both agree will instantly stop the action. It's clearest if the word you choose is unrelated to sex, for example, 'Freezer' could be good for indicating '*Stop right now!*' with 'Fridge' being a warning signal if things are beginning to get uncomfortable. Saying the actual word 'Stop' isn't such a good idea, as pleading for mercy can be part of the fun, so decide on something that works for the two of you. You need to have a code word that's not open to any misinterpretation, so if either of you is upset or uncomfortable, you can both stop play *immediately* – without prior explanation.

Knock three times

Of course, if either of you has your mouth covered as part of the game, you will need a physical sign, such as banging on the floor three times with a hand or foot, to indicate similarly that you want to stop. So make sure you always have either your mouth or a limb free to give an agreed stop signal.

Wetting your appetite

Urolagnia – otherwise known as urophilia, golden showers or watersports – is a sexual fetish focussing on urine and urination. It's regarded as one of the more taboo sexual acts, but indulging in something that's perceived as humiliating and dirty gives many people a powerfully erotic release. There can be an illicit thrill in watching someone pee or wet their pants (hence the countless websites and porn films devoted to the subject) though it seems to be more of a man-watching-woman thing than the other way around!

If it does appeal to you, it's obviously practical to experiment in the bathroom or outdoors. Drinking loads of water or fruit juice will dilute your urine and make it smell sweeter, but steer well clear of asparagus, and apparently peas can make your pee smell dodgy too.

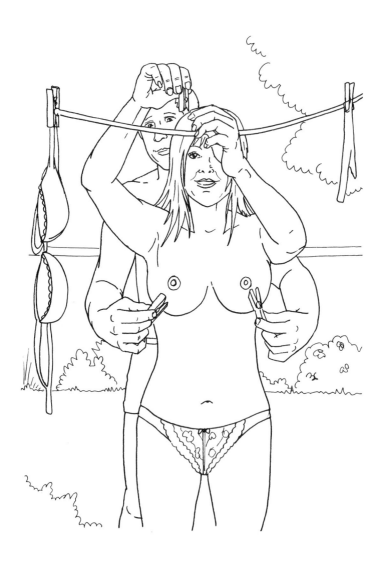

A bit nippy

Nipple clamps are a popular S&M sex toy – for both sexes. First build up tolerance with nipple play – teasing, squeezing, sucking and pulling – before investing in a set of clips or clamps (and never wear them for longer than 20 minutes at a time). Bear in mind too that for women, nipple clamps can feel good or not according to where they are in their menstrual cycle. Household pegs are a good value substitute for basic training. Experiment with wood and plastic – you can always stretch the metal spring to make it gentler if it hurts too much.

Six favourite fetishes

For many people, the world of fetishism isn't a game, it's more a way of life. A fetish is the sexual admiration of a specific, often inanimate object, that becomes necessary for erotic gratification. The whole subordination/domination scene has very strict safety guidelines, and S&M devotees can manipulate their bodily sensations so they experience an endorphin high when pain is administered. If you'd like to dip your toe into a more sexually adventurous arena, here are your starters for six …

1. Spanking (with palms, paddles or the back of a hairbrush).
2. Cross-dressing (women's underwear – as worn by mostly heterosexual men).
3. Foot fetishism (bare feet, stilettos and sky-high boots – to be licked all over).
4. Being flogged (whipped with leather, suede, rubber etc.)
5. Wearing rubber, leather, PVC or latex.
6. Medical procedures and devices (enemas, dental braces and shiny steel probes).

chapter 11
Toys & playtime

Shopping for sex toys has never been easier – whether you prefer to buy online, or to be hands-on and handle before buying – there are now sex shops in High Streets all over the country. Either way, if you're in a relationship, try choosing toys together if you can – it's not only fun, it can be a turn-on too.

If you feel safer just ordering online, there are several excellent companies giving frank and honest customer feedback – and your goodies should arrive in anonymous brown packages (so no blushes as the postman hands you your parcel!).

The range on offer is impressive, with everything from whips to anal beads, lipstick vibrators to I'd-never-get-that-thing-inside-me dildos. Because there is so much on offer, and because it can be a little confusing, here are a few examples that I think are adult toy box essentials, and a couple of newcomers that are well on their way to being ...

Live wire

For a spot of mutual massage check out vibrating condom rings. Worn with or without a condom, they're a penile accessory that fits around the base of the shaft, and which sport a little vibrating bullet to stimulate the clitoris during intercourse. Enjoy experimenting with positions that maximise clitoral contact – a grinding motion works particularly well.

Prepping up

If you're planning a special session to play with any new toys, it helps to have all your various bits close at hand — maybe even lay them out like chefs lay out their ingredients?! It's a real passion killer having to stop the fun because you've left the lube in the bathroom, or you need a new pack of batteries — much better to prepare in advance, then you can stay focussed on the job in hand.

Sauce material

Lube is a classic bedroom essential, and probably the best, most liberating sex-toy in the world. It can enrich every sexual experience by swapping friction for flow. Yet the latest statistics from Durex claim that 75% of adults believe lubricants are only used for vaginal dryness — and 63% associate lubricants with anal sex.

Although it is *crucial* to use lube for anal sex (as the anus has no natural lubrication of its own) and lube does do wonders for dry spells down below (see *Slip slidin' away*, page 129) it also enhances masturbation, oral sex, nipple play, massage, and vibe-play. Plus it elevates a hand-job from alright to awe-inspiring in a few slick strokes.

Your lube low-down …

Lubricants fall into three basic types: water-based, silicone-based, and oil-based.

Water-based feel the most natural – they're the ones that most closely mimic a woman's own juices. They don't stain, they're safe for use with latex, and they rarely cause irritation. They can sometimes dry out if you're going at it like the clappers, but they're quickly revived with a spritz of water or a little saliva, and they're good for both vaginal and anal sex – plus they wash off easily when you've finished playing.

Silicone-based lubes retain their lubricating properties better and longer than water-based ones and they're highly concentrated, so a little goes a long way – meaning they're the favourite for anal sex, as they're thick and latex-friendly. They're oil-free too, so no stains, and they're great for massage (and as a shaving oil – for his chin and her pins!). Silicone lubes are also completely waterproof, making them ideal for use in showers and hot-tubs. The only downside is that you can't use silicone lubes with silicone toys (because any silicone molecules will eventually rot each other) and they're a little more difficult to clean off than water-based lubes.

Oil-based lubes are great for anal sex, male foreplay and masturbation. On the plus side, they're very long lasting and never become sticky, but what's not so good about them is that they're not recommended for vaginal use, and they tend to stain fabrics. Like Vaseline, moisturisers and baby oil, they destroy latex, so they should never be used with diaphragms or condoms.

So that's a basic run-down. There are lots of manufacturers out there creating spicy variations to add fun and flavour to your new lube-life, including warming ones, ones that tingle, and ones in sugar-free, dye-free flavours.

There's no excuse for leaving lube out of your toy-box — it's not just a woman-thing — it can improve *both* your sex lives across the board. All you've got to do now is think of some ingenious ways to apply your Strawberry and Kiwi or Tantalising Tangerine ... how about popping a bit somewhere on your body, blindfolding your partner, then getting them to find it with their tongue ... ?

A little bit of shut-eye …

Buy a special eye mask – or keep one of those issued as a freebie on some flights. Not just useful for a quick snooze, but equally suitable as a sexy blindfold.

If one of our senses is taken away it tends to heighten the others, so now's a good moment for some extra-sensory experimentation. Ask your lover to try stroking you with a feather (deliciously tingly if you can get beyond the tickle-factor) or explore the different ways they can touch and stimulate you. Get them to whisper their most secret fantasies in your ear – it's somehow easier to reveal all when you can't be seen, and very liberating if you both surrender to the experience.

Try this for size

Stiff root vegetables like carrots, parsnips, courgettes, and cucumbers make convenient, cheap dildos and butt plugs – but make sure you wash them thoroughly to get rid of any pesticides – or peel them if you'd prefer (even cover them with a condom for maximum safety). To paraphrase some sound advice from the self-pleasure pioneer Betty Dodson "If you're peeling a cucumber, remember to leave some of the skin at the bottom to act as a handle, and don't carve too close to the seeds or your cucumber may lose its erection".

Europhiles may be pleased to hear that recent EU regulations are seeking straight cucumbers with minimum curvature – great for anal or if you like your penetration deep. Brings a whole new meaning to getting your five a day …

I-scream!

The Cone is the modern-day equivalent of that old favourite, the spin cycle on a washing machine – except in compact form that's a bit easier to transport. (Having said that, it's not exactly a discreet little number that you pop in your sponge bag, hoping it'll go unnoticed.)

As vibrators go, it's a big one, but it needs to be – it's hands-free and sits solidly on the floor, so you can squirm around happily on its point. You can then take yourself through each of its 16 pulsating, vibrating settings, and if you get impatient, just press the shortcut 'Orgasm Button' (one thing my washing machine doesn't have!).

It was originally designed as part of an S&M chair, but apparently proved to be far too comfortable for pain lovers. There's a big buzz about this one – literally – but a lot of it is muffled when you're sitting on it, and I haven't had so many laughs with a toy in ages. A cone that really puts you in the zone.

The vibrator

There are hundreds of vibrators out there – clitoral 'bullets', curved G-spot vibes, anal ones, awful ones ... The choices are endless – in terms of size, speed, material, colour, versatility, price, how lifelike, how easy to use, and what's the noise-level? (Meaning will you ever be able to look your neighbours in the eye again?)

Vibrators have revolutionised the female orgasm – and they've not done too badly for the male one either (his perineum seems to be the favourite hot-spot – the skin between his balls and his anus). Apparently it takes an average of 20 minutes for women to climax through masturbation, oral sex, or penetration, but using a vibrator can make us come in anything from 60 seconds to 3 minutes – about the same time it takes to make a cuppa in fact.

No wonder they were the fifth household appliance to be electrified – beaten only by the sewing machine, fan, kettle, and toaster.

Rampant Rabbit – the vital statistics

When the Rabbit made its now legendary appearance in
Sex and the City, it licensed millions of women to go forth and
wave their bunnies in the air. Vibrators were out in the open –
no longer something that you hid at the bottom of your knicker
drawer. Suddenly everyone was talking about them – even men,
who became more cliterate almost overnight.

The Rabbit is now the most famous sex toy in the world.
Ann Summer's has seven different models of it's Rampant Rabbit
hopping into homes all over the country, and whether you're
a bunny fan or not, it's a toy you can't ignore. The latest models
to hit the headlines are:

- The Thriller – purple, 5-speeds, with futuristic nodules all
  over it.

- The Thruster – blue, 6-speeds, with a ruthless pistoning action.

- The Platinum – sexy silver, 6-speeds, with 7 modes of clit
  vibration.

- The Three way – pink, 5-speeds, with an anal stimulator to
  give you trigasms (yup, that's three orgasms for the price
  of one!).

All have the famous clit-hugging ears, and offer a myriad of vibe
permutations – and after spending an afternoon with the whole
family I did have a bit of difficulty walking. Can't decide which
I like best – which means I'm just going to have to start all over
again ... it's hard, it really is.

New friend

I was going to write a tip about the merits of the electric toothbrush as an aid to self-gratification (as well as its more obvious role in our bathrooms). They've now hit the headlines though as a legitimate sexcessory, because of a pert little gadget called Brush Bunny. Shocking pink and sporting those famous rabbit ears, Brush Bunny eases his silicone body over your toothbrush head, and conveniently vibrates at the ideal speed to have you hopping with joy. Because of his colour he's also easy to pass off as a kid's toy or novelty pen-topper, so minimum embarrassment if he's a travelling companion and your suitcase is searched at the airport.

"I'm sorry madam, I'm going to have to quarantine him."

Gender-bender

Strap-ons are becoming increasingly popular – they always have been in the world of girl-on-girl sex, but there's now a new phenomenon of couples wanting to try female to male penetration. It's called 'pegging' (don't ask me why) and one of the latest dildos to hit the headlines is the eye-watering Tantus Feeldoe Stout Vibrating Double Dildo – quite a mouthful, in more ways than one.

A strap-on can look strangely thrilling on a woman, even if it's just for show. Normally the woman has to wear a harness or specially designed pants to keep the dildo in place, but this one doesn't need either – the wearer fits the smaller bulbous end of it into her vagina, leaving the dildo protruding (think bendy straw with the long bit shaped like a penis). You need powerful PC muscles to do the job of keeping it there (and if they're not powerful now, they sure as hell soon will be!).

On page 91, *Delve a little deeper*, I give practical guidelines on anal intercourse, all of which applies to pegging too – but do make sure you use loads of thick *water*-based lubricant (silicone-based lubes destroy silicone toys).

Feeldoe was designed by a woman, for women – which is why it has little ridges thoughtfully positioned for clitoral stimulation for the wearer, and both parties can relish the skin-on-skin intimacy it offers. This might not be for everyone, but for a lot of women – and men – it's a huge turn-on. It's about the closest a girl can get to having a willy without growing one of her own.

Pass go and collect …

If you're secretly craving to put that hotel down on Mayfair but it's not your loved one's idea of a fun night in, dim the lights and set up instead for a steamy game of Monogamy – A Hot Affair … With Your Partner! Voted 'Adult Game of the Year', it's packed with raunchy, inventive ideas to inject excitement and desire into a relationship. It's full of surprises and humour, and is quite an eye-opener – however well you think you know each other! Just like Monopoly you might not make it to the end either … You'll get addicted, I promise.

Over-powering

A word of warning girls: beware overuse of your rabbit, cone, or any other vibrator. Vibes can be addictive, and your – or his – good old trusted finger might begin to lose its appeal after protracted use of a battery-powered friend. Toys should be an extension of love-play, to add variety, but not to replace the human touch.

chapter 12
Trouble shooting?

There are certain times in everyone's lives when body parts refuse to co-operate. It's frustrating when they're attached to you and they were working just fine yesterday, but if we don't panic, they often put themselves right and we're left with only a little dented pride. For example, 60% of men over the age of 35 experience erectile problems at some stage, and scores of women lose their libidos because of stress, tiredness, low self-esteem, or a whole combination of reasons.

Many problems arise with long-term relationships when the initial novelty wears off – libidos can nose-dive, and you have to work at turning yourselves and each other on, because desire is no longer a given.

Successful long-term sex is fuelled by a mixture of effort, intimacy, skill, and imagination – all kneaded together with the magic ingredient of time. That's a commodity most of us have in short supply, but we can overcome challenges and salvage ailing sex lives if we use it wisely, and are supportive and patient with each other. There's no substitute for being open and honest and talking things through. "What can I do to make things work?" is a great place to start.

Does my bum look big in this?

Interestingly, men are far less focussed on a woman's physical faults than we are ourselves – they really don't scrutinise our cellulite bottoms like we do. Try not to obsess about wobbles, or whatever worries you, as that can be a turn-off in itself.

Can't come, won't come?

If you're a bloke who's having trouble ejaculating during intercourse, but the problem doesn't occur when you're masturbating, it may be to do with the way you're actually pleasuring yourself. If your technique is to squeeze your penis hard, or stroke it really fast, a vagina isn't ever going to match up to what your hand can achieve. You need to re-educate your organ to respond to a far lighter touch. Start by not masturbating for a week (or as long as you can manage!) then when you do, stroke yourself softly and slowly, using only your fingertips and maybe a little lubricant. The next time you make love should be explosive …

Scientific success

Hailed as female Viagra and garnering good reviews, Zestra is a female arousal fluid that's been clinically proven to heighten intimate sensation and satisfaction. Comprising all natural botanical ingredients (primarily starflower and evening primrose oils) it's massaged into the vulva five minutes before the fun starts, and the pleasurable warming effect lasts about 45 minutes. It's not cheap, but reports indicate it can increase desire and provide more intense, speedier orgasms – even for women suffering a loss of libido for any reason.

Another product to help with upping your orgasm quota is Tracey Cox's Supersex Orgasm Gel. It contains arginine, an amino acid which also increases arousal – and turbo-charges the tingle down below.

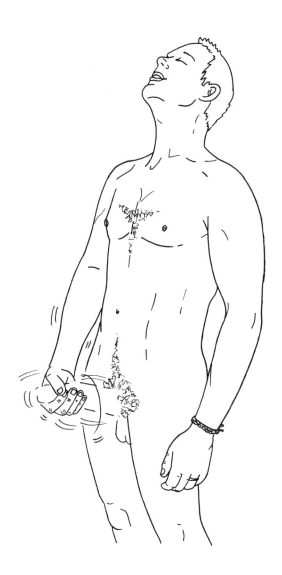

"DEFINITELY tonight, Josephine!"

Scent of a woman

Every woman has her own unique taste and scent – her own aromatic signature. It's well-known that Napoleon used to prefer Josephine when she was a little savoury ("Don't wash, I'm coming home" was a favourite command) and healthy female love juices are a considerable turn-on for most men.

However, if you're washing regularly but you're conscious of a bad or unnaturally pungent genital smell, do get it checked out with your doctor or a clinic to make sure there aren't any underlying medical issues. If you're OK but the problem continues, take a look at your diet and lifestyle; stress, heavy drinking, smoking, and a lot of spicy, animal or dairy products can all affect us vaginally (basically the same foods that influence our breath and body odour).

Avoid any lubes or body lotions that are petroleum-based as they can clog you up, and so-called 'intimate' sprays or scented douches can not only disrupt our natural balance of flora and fauna, but they also disguise our own inherent musk. You could end up smelling more like a cleaning product than a person, and old Boney would certainly have sniffed at that ...

Ring me ...

If your penis loses the plot in the middle of the action, find help in the form of a penile constrictor ring, worn around the base of the shaft. They convert a weak erection into a strong one by enhancing blood flow, and can also delay ejaculation – but never wear them for more than 20 minutes at a time, and be careful if you are diabetic or have circulatory problems.

Choose carefully, as one that's too small runs the risk of getting stuck (so flexible silicone is better for beginners than a metal or leather cock ring) and lube up first for easy removal. Some guys may prefer to adorn their tackle with a ring that embraces the balls as well – try putting it on before you're erect too, to savour the feeling of tightness as you get hard.

DIY SOS

The female genitals are their own self-cleaning eco-system. More hygienic than many other parts of the body, including the mouth, they've been described as being as healthy as a carton of yoghurt! This might seem an odd comparison, but the kind of healthy bacteria found in yoghurt – lactobacilli – are also present in vaginal secretions, which is why eating natural, unsweetened yoghurt can help stave off vaginal infections, or restore the correct balance when an infection is present. And there's more than one way of taking it – try putting some on a panty-liner at bedtime to ease the symptoms of thrush. Just make sure it's the plain, unflavoured variety containing live cultures (mandarin orange might seem more appealing, but it won't do the trick!).

Speed limits

Premature ejaculation is the most common sexual problem for men, but it can be successfully cured by squeezing the penis just below the head when you're close to coming, using a stop/start technique when masturbating, or by visualising deeply unsexy images. Guys can also delay their urge to climax by using a condom, such as Performa, that contains a tiny amount of local anaesthetic cream in the tip. The cream de-sensitises the penis head, so intercourse can last longer.

Slip slidin' away

Many factors can cause vaginal dryness – it's a very common condition. Just because you're not wet it doesn't mean you're not interested. It's also possible to be dripping one minute and then dry the next (this often happens after climaxing).

The amount of natural lubrication a woman produces varies according to oestrogen levels, and can be affected by your menstrual cycle, childbirth, breastfeeding, or the menopause. Medications like antihistamines, antidepressants and the Pill, together with your stress levels and how much you drink and smoke, can also have an influence. Adding saliva to your own juices is a help, but spit dries out quickly when it's exposed to air, so keep a glass of water nearby to moisten your mouth. Better still, invest in one of the umpteen specially formulated personal lubricants now on the market – these can transform painful intercourse into slippery bliss, and they're great for pleasuring both of you. There is a wide selection of lubes available, including several new varieties that tingle and taste great. (Also see *Sauce Material*, page 108.)

chapter 13
Nature's helpers

Named after Aphrodite, the Greek goddess of love, an aphrodisiac is something that claims to arouse or increase sexual desire. Almost anything can have aphrodisiac qualities, but we generally think of them as being something that you eat or drink. They can also be used to improve your performance, or to ward off exhaustion if you intend banging away all night.

Wholesome nourishing foods such as shellfish, honey, eggs, seeds, and nuts have traditionally been regarded as the most reliable stimulants – possibly because they compensated for a nutrient-poor diet in some cultures. Aphrodisiacs were also believed to increase fertility, and thought to have sensual powers because of their smell, texture, or shape. An open fig can resemble a woman's vulva, an oyster can feel or smell like male and female love juices, and bananas, carrots, eels, and asparagus all have an obviously phallic appearance.

If you're thinking of experimenting with some of Nature's helpers, remember that the very act of preparing treats for someone and 'setting the scene' is in itself a loving gesture. We can enhance our erotic enjoyment by appealing to all our senses – lighting, fragrance, music, and a relaxing atmosphere can all contribute. Try abandoning the cutlery and feeding each other with your fingers too – so much sexier.

Exploring aphrodisiacs, whether they're folklore or fact, can be a catalyst for added excitement in a relationship – and I bet you'll have a few laughs in the process. Who cares if they're a myth – so long as they add a little magic.

Girl-talk

I've always loved that old joke 'What do you put behind your ears to attract the men? Answer: your ankles ... ' On a more serious note though, if you're very comfortable with your own scent, your personal 'cassolette' (the French term for how you smell down below) there's something very exciting for your mate if you dab a little of yourself behind your ears. Forget expensive perfume, a little bit of unique, pheromone-packed 'Me No. 5' can go a long way – plus it's free and always to hand!

Goat for it ...

A herbal supplement that deserves a mention is the aptly-named Horny Goat Weed, christened centuries ago by a Chinese goat herder who noticed that his randy goats couldn't keep their hooves off each other whenever they chewed a certain weed. Used for over 2,000 years in Asia as a traditional remedy for liver, kidney, and joint disorders, it's gained a reputation in the West as a sexual cure-all and carnal firecracker.

Willy vanilly

Vanilla has long been regarded as a sensual stimulant. The sex researcher, Havelock Ellis, made the discovery that employees in a vanilla pod factory were in a constant state of lewd arousal – apparently its aroma increases blood flow to the penis by 8%.

Good job they weren't harvesting lavender – a whiff of that accounts for a sizeable 18% engorgement in the male nether regions ... what a waste to keep that sachet scenting your drawers.

The old ones …

The *Kama Sutra* offers a recipe that claims to make the reader "strong for the act of love and disposed to lying together". It suggests a goat's or ram's testicle boiled in sweetened milk, served with buttered, honeyed rice, and a side dish of sparrows' eggs. Legend has it that Aphrodite considered sparrows to be sacred because of their "amorous nature", and for that reason they were often an ingredient in various erotic brews.

… are maybe not the best!

While a recipe from *The Perfumed Garden*, a 16th century Arabic treatise, recommends a glass of very thick honey, with 100 pine nuts and 20 almonds, to be taken for three nights at bedtime – just make sure you also book an appointment with your dentist.

Sow your wild oats

Testosterone is known to be a powerful hormone responsible for libido and performance, in women as well as men. Oatmeal is thought to help release and activate it, as wild oats contain an enzyme that frees up 'bound' testosterone in the body, with women reporting an increased sex drive and men displaying firmer erections. The three bears certainly knew what was good for them – so make porridge, muesli, or oatcakes part of your daily diet.

Sin and tonic

An ancient energy-giver that's still going strong is ginseng. For centuries, men in Asia have been using it to boost their sexual performance, increase stamina, and treat erectile dysfunction. The word literally means 'man root' and, aside from its uncanny resemblance to the human body, recent tests in China show that it also increases testosterone in both sexes, as well as being a powerful, rejuvenating tonic. So go grab that ginseng, especially the potent Red Korean variety. You won't grow a beard girls – and you'll be dynamite between the sheets.

Herbal viagra?

Muira Puama is a herbal stimulant extracted from the roots and bark of the rainforest trees in Brazil – in fact it's called 'potency wood' in South America because of the punch it packs. Dr. Jacques Waynberg, from the Institute of Sexology in Paris, has found it to be effective for attaining and maintaining an erection by increasing blood flow to the penis, and for reviving sexually jaded appetites in both sexes – so it helps psychologically as well as physically. It's also used for staving off rheumatism and baldness, making it one very versatile herb!

One for the boys

It may not be an obvious aphrodisiac, but celery can really get things going when it's eaten by men. Celery contains androsterone, a hormone released by men when they sweat, and it's a considerable turn-on for women. So don't dodge the salad boys – this one may have more benefits than just a slimmer waist.

Ready heady go!

Certain essential oils are reputed to be sexually stimulating, so pop a few drops into a bath and take a soak, preferably with your partner. Try jasmine, ylang ylang, rose, sandalwood, and juniper to really get you in the mood – either separately or as a cocktail. Experiment with the mix, or add a few drops to a neutral massage oil for some seriously sensual stroking

Wine wisdom

A moderate quantity of wine is considered to have an aphrodisiac effect. Opinions differ as to whether red or white works better, so the obvious thing is to follow your preference. Choose quality over quantity though, as too much alcohol of any kind can leave you grinding to a flaccid halt. Drink enough to loosen inhibitions and clothing, and then stop before sleep starts to seem like a preferable option!

Sensuous fruit

The Aztecs called the avocado tree 'Ahuacuatl' meaning 'testicle tree' and avocados were thought to be so potent that, in the words of Cynthia Watson M.D., the Aztec culture "forbade village maidens to set one virginal toe outside the house while the fruit was being gathered". It's true, avocados do resemble a pair of balls when they're hanging in pairs on the tree, but there's much more to them than meets the eye. Not only are they delicious, they're also packed with folic acid, vitamin B6, and potassium, giving you both energy and a libido lift. Try some balsamic vinegar on their slippery flesh – eat them with your hands, then lick it off each other's fingers ...

Biological benefits

The Aztecs were first in line to celebrate chocolate, holding riotous orgies to honour the harvest of the cacao bean. Chocolate contains PEA, or phenylethylamine, which is the same chemical that gives us the euphoric feeling we experience when we're newly in love. It's also full of antioxidants (the enzymes that help prevent cancer) and a caffeine-related substance called theobromine. For maximum benefit, the general rule of thumb is the darker the better, with at least 70% cocoa solids – and sod the calories.

Ten top turn-ons to improve diminished desires

1. **Oysters** – Highly nutritious, low in fat and loaded with zinc, which escalates production of sperm and testosterone. One of the classics. Shuck 'n' fuck.

2. **Cucumber** – Dr Alan Hirsch, director of the Smell and Taste Research Foundation in Chicago, has discovered that women are hugely aroused by the smell of cucumber (not to mention being quite partial to their design ...).

3. **Banana bread** – Another stimulating aroma from Dr Hirsch's findings. Also well designed, bananas are rich in potassium and energising B vitamins, but it may be the 'comforting and nostalgic smell' of banana bread that helps 'women feel more relaxed'. (And extremely hungry.)

4. **Cinnamon** – Emerged as the favourite male whiff in Dr H's scientific study of over 200 smells. Inhaling it gets blood racing to the penis, and cinnamon buns are particularly popular. Get baking girls ...

5. **Beetroot** – Chris Moore, voted 'Sexiest Farmer in the North' by the National Farmers' Union, claims that beetroot gets you bonking. It contains high levels of the mineral boron, thought to influence the manufacture of human sex hormones. Mr Moore's theory was endorsed when he spotted a beetroot depicted in the wall-paintings of an ancient brothel in Pompeii.

6. **It's the pits** – The pheromonal oomph of a clean, *freshly* exercised armpit ... sniff and sigh happy.

7. **Liquorice** – the strong, serious black kind. Chewing the root gives rise to lustful urges and makes women particularly wanton. You'll never look at Allsorts in the same way again.

8. **Almonds** – A perennial symbol of fertility, almonds – like chocolate – are blessed with bags of phenylethylamine, the feel-good amino acid. They're also a first-rate source of essential fatty acids (good for male hormone production) and their smell is said to provoke passion in the fairer sex. Double marzipan on the Christmas cake then.

9. **Damiana** – A centuries-old South American aphrodisiac that can be taken as a supplement or drunk as a tea. Damiana contains gonzalitosin, which creates a feeling of gentle elation and a pleasant throbbing in his loins. Is that Damiana in your pocket – or are you just pleased to see me?

10. **Putting the accent on sex** – OK, you might feel like a wally at first, but if she melts when you talk like Robert de Niro – or he can't get enough of your Mariella Frostrup impression – where's the harm in humouring your loved one? A sexy voice resonates in more ways than one. After all, how many babies have been conceived with backing vocals provided by Barry White? I rest my case.

A final piece of wisdom from P. J. O'Rourke

"There are a number of mechanical devices which increase sexual arousal, particularly in women. Chief among these is the Mercedes-Benz 380SL Convertible."

"Why, thank you kind Sir. I should be delighted to make love with you."

chapter 14
Etiquette & playing safe

The idea of safer sex is nothing new, but its importance should never be underestimated. When you have unprotected sex with someone, you're effectively also having it with all the previous partners they've had unprotected sex with – so using the 'family tree' principle, you're sharing body fluids – and risks – with countless others. Scary.

To quote Suzi Godson, from her comprehensive *The Sex Book*, "The exchange of bodily fluids, however pleasant, has always been a dangerous occupation ... teenagers sometimes believe that 'safe sex' simply means their parents won't catch them".

Misconceptions are still far too common, contributing to the widespread increase of HIV and sexually transmitted infections (STIs), many of which have no visible symptoms. You can't always tell if someone's a carrier – so do get tested if you're worried about yourself at all. There's no way of knowing someone's sexual health from their outward appearance, so the only safe option is to take proper precautions against diseases – and pregnancy – and to discuss these precautions before you're overcome with desire.

Safe sex overlaps into etiquette – the right thing is *always* to be safety conscious. If we're out there having sex with new or different partners, we should all – men and women – be in possession of condoms and never be shy about using them. It's crazy not to. Stay in control, minimise the risks, and take responsibility for your sexual health and well being.

A word of warning

If a vibrator or toy has an overpoweringly plastic smell when you open its box, don't use it without a condom. Phthalates are a class of chemical contaminants that are added to plastics to make them soft and pliable, and unfortunately many sex toys contain them. Laws were passed years ago restricting the type of plastics that could be used in baby toys – but there is currently no legislation over sex toys. Rule of thumb – if it pongs, put a rubber on it.

Patience please

If there's something you like – a sexual activity or position – that your partner isn't good at, be careful how you tell them. Make sure any criticism is *always* constructive so they can learn and improve. Harsh words that undermine and destroy precious confidence aren't going to win anyone any prizes, and insensitive comments will hurt and stay with them – what's more, they won't want to try it again!

The key to fulfilment for both of you is in communication. Explain, teach and *show* each other what you enjoy, and give loads of praise and encouragement along the way. It also helps to use 'I' statements, as in 'I don't feel good about that' or 'I love it when you do that', which enable you to take responsibility and remove pressure away from your partner. Be honest – but be gentle and tactful.

No-blow zone

It's fun to experiment, but be careful *never* to blow air into the vagina during oral sex – the outcome could be fatal. There is a danger it could create an air bubble, or embolus, that might obstruct the flow of blood through a vein or artery. Not worth the risk.

Ow!

However generously endowed your man may be, never try bending his erect penis – believe it or not, it can break. You may well think of it as collapsible, but it's not designed to fold away!

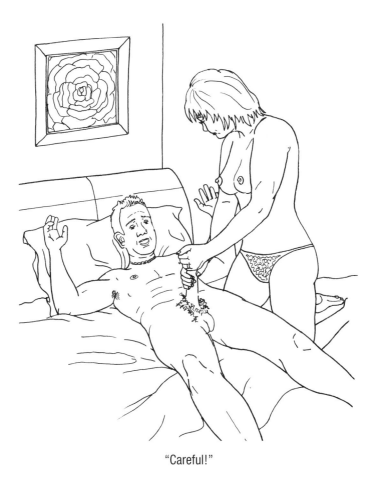

"Careful!"

Sugar 'n' spice

Don't insert any edibles into the vagina that might burn (like spicy foods), get stuck (marrow?!) or be difficult to retrieve (like grapes). Another no-no from the fruit bowl is a peeled banana, as it disintegrates easily. Your local greengrocer can supply far better substitute dildos (see *Try this for size*, page 113) and also the high sugar content of bananas can lead to yeast infections like thrush.

"So tell me darling, what did happen to the cucumber in the fridge?"

The same goes for any sweet foods that may interfere with the sensitive pH balance down below, including chocolate. Keep your choc-fix above waist level, as the oil in it can burn holes in latex condoms and chocolate can also leave embarrassing brown streaks on your sheets – slightly worrying for a new partner!

Do's and don'ts for rubber goods

The best way to protect yourself is by using condoms. Actually, the best way to protect yourself is by using condoms correctly. They're inexpensive and available everywhere, so here are some useful do's & don'ts ...

Do use a condom *every time*. They prevent unwanted pregnancy and protect against unwanted STIs and HIV – plus the range of all-singing, all-dancing, pleasure-enhancing varieties is extensive.

Do check the expiry date. Old condoms are more likely to split.

Do store them carefully, away from heat, wallets, pockets, and car glove compartments.

Do follow the instructions for putting on the condom; it's a process both sides can get involved in.

Don't wait until it's too late. If your bits are near your partner's bits, you should be wearing a condom.

Don't risk damaging a condom by using your teeth to open the packet.

Don't linger too long after the party's over – pull out as soon as you've come, with your penis still erect, and holding the rubber ring at the base.

Don't flush! Latex is a notorious drain clogger. Tie a knot in it, admire your virility – then bin it.

Four things not to have in your bedroom

1. **A television**. Studies have shown it can seriously reduce your nooky levels if you're desperate to catch *EastEnders* – or whatever turns you on. You run the risk of just not turning each other on. The electromagnetic field around TVs doesn't make for sweet dreams either.

2. **Photos of friends and family.** It's not easy to lose yourself in a thundering orgasm if your mum and dad are grinning at you from your bedside table. Much as you love them – and your angelic offspring – monumental sex will be more achievable if they're not watching, so make a home for them elsewhere.

3. **Mess.** Meaning all our junk and clutter which often ends up on the floor. And don't just shove it under the bed either – it makes for a high sneeze factor and causes stagnant energy to be trapped. In Feng Shui terms (the ancient oriental art of placement) this can lead to health problems and disturbed nights (but not in the way you'd want them to be). Manky knickers and soiled sheets may have worked brilliantly for Tracy Emin, but they're generally not top of the list for a good sex life, so freshen up now.

4. **Single images.** Another Feng Shui tip is to avoid pictures portraying a single person or image, as this may then be reflected in your relationships – or lack of them. Pictures of couples are a far more positive influence in a bedroom, promoting equality and harmony. So whether you're looking for a relationship or wanting to sustain one, surround yourself with pairs rather than singles.

Recommended reading …

SEX by numbers
by Sarah Hedley
ISBN: 978-0749926960

The Sex Book
by Suzi Godson with
Mel Agace
ISBN: 978-1844035113

Superhotsex
by Tracey Cox
ISBN: 978-0756622756

*Tickle His Pickle – Your Hands-
On Guide to Penis Pleasing*
by Dr. Sadie Allison
ISBN: 978-0970661128

Sex for One
by Betty Dodson, Ph.D.
ISBN: 978-0517886076

*'O' The Intimate
Story of the Orgasm*
by Jonathan Margolis
ISBN: 978-0099441557

Incredible Sex
by Marcelle Perks and
Elisabeth Wilson
SBN: 978-1904902331

Hot Sex – How to Do It
by Tracey Cox
ISBN: 978-0552147071

*She Comes First –
The Thinking Man's Guide
to Pleasuring a Woman*
by Ian Kerner, Ph.D.
ISBN: 978-0285637221

*269 amazing sex tips
and tricks for men*
by Anne Hooper and
Phillip Hodson
ISBN: 978-1861059581

*"Ann Summers" Raunchy and
Rampant Guide to Sex Toys*
by Ann Summers
ISBN: 978-0091916435

*How to Give Her
Absolute Pleasure*
by Lou Paget
ISBN: 978-0749922627

Tricks to Please a Woman
by Jay Wiseman
ISBN: 978-1890159405

XXX Sex Tonight!
by Anne Hooper
ISBN: 978-0756615246

The Book of Weird Sex
by Chris Gordon
ISBN: 978-0749083465

The Kama Sutra of Vatsyayana
by Sir Richard Burton
ISBN: 978-0486452371

Women's Pleasure
by Rachel Swift
ISBN: 978-0330333252

"Cosmopolitan":
Over 100 Triple X Sex Tricks
by Lisa Sussman
ISBN: 978-1844424801

Great Sex Techniques
by Linda Sonntag
ISBN: 978-0600606185

The Doctors' Book of Home
Remedies for Women
by Sharon Faelten
ISBN: 978-0875963433

Thanks to ...

There are many people who have helped in the writing of this book and my collective thanks to you all (as some of you don't want to be individually named!)

MY SPECIAL THANKS HOWEVER TO THE FOLLOWING:

Steve and **Anne Brookes** at Public Eye Publications for their support, patience, sandwiches, and faith in me; **Tracy Staskevich** for her witty illustrations – and her style, humour, vision, and constant encouragement; **Bronwyn Robertson** for her wisdom, proofing skills and advice.

I am very grateful to **Sarah Hedley** for her kindness in writing the foreword, and to **Tracey Cox**, **Dr. Catherine Hood**, **Jenni Trent Hughes** and **Mimo Antonucci** for their endorsements. Thanks too to my wonderful agent **Julia Chapman**, and all **the team at NCI** – especially **Jo Wander** and Nicola Ibison.

Huge thanks to my treasured family and friends, for their love and belief in me, which has meant so much. My daughter **Kate McEnery**, my sister **Lilian**, and my brother **David** have all been amazing. Thanks too to **Bridget Brice**(BB), **Sha**, **David Charles** and **Mufrida Hayes**, **Victoria**, **Dom** and **Sharon**, **Jane**, **The GG's**, **Simon Rimmer**, **Polly**, **Sue** and **Adrian**, **Franko**, **Helen**, **Mikhail**, **NRJ**, **Cath B**, **Laura Tucker**, **Jos** and **Steve**, **Sandra**, **Alex**, **Snuff**, **Gary** in Grimsby, **Barry** in 'Romany's', **Sam** in 'Secrets', and **Jackie Llewelyn-Bowen** and **Mary Danson-Hill** in 'Charmed.'

And I'm particularly grateful to **Jan Holt**, **Penny** and **Vince**, **Lindsay Henson**, **Trevor McCallum**, **Jess Greatrex**, **Da'aboth Te'he'Ling**, **Maggie Kruger**, **Wendy Turner-Webster** and **Kevin Dunn**, for their extra-special support.

Thanks to **Megan Roberts** at *www.idlubricants co.uk* for her shining enthusiasm; **Christy** and **Lizzy** at Ann Summers for being so welcoming and helpful; **Angela Sonenscher** and **Maeva** at Soho's Paradiso Boudoir for their insights and honesty; **Angela Marriella Pascale** (aka Cindy Sins) for being totally outrageous; and **Ruth Wilkinson** and **Richard Longhurst** at *www.lovehoney.co.uk* for their frankness, help and astounding delivery speeds!

THANKS ALSO TO THE FOLLOWING COMPANIES
FOR THEIR GENEROSITY:

The team at *www.sensualessentials.com*
Amanda Barnett at *www.blissbox.com*
Sarah-Louise Heslop and **Sonia Marshall** at *www.durex.com*
Richie and **Jane Bowles** at *www.monogamyonline.com*
Jan Dutton at *www.smoothshave.co.uk*
Martyn Maxey at *www.martynmaxey.com*
Risë Rytlewski at *www.instead.uk.com*
and the teams at *www.bondagetape.com,*
www.sh-womenstore.com
and *www.scarletmagazine.co.uk.*

And last but never least, I am most grateful to my husband **Patrick Pearson**, for his brilliant editing skills, for his gentleness, and for always remaining calm. Thank you for being adventurous enough to test numerous toys with me; for putting up with me when I've been stressed and horrible; for cooking the best roast chicken in the world; and for making me laugh so much.

143 Always x

Index

'The Greatest Tips in the World' books

Household Tips
by Vicky Burford
ISBN 978-1-905151-02-8

DIY Tips
by Chris Jones & Brian Lee
ISBN 978-1-905151-03-5

Cookery Tips
by Peter Osborne
ISBN 978-1-905151-04-2

Golfing Tips
by John Cook
ISBN 978-1-905151-05-9

Gardening Tips
by Steve Brookes
ISBN 978-1-905151-06-6

Yoga Tips
by D. Gellineau & D. Robson
ISBN 978-1-905151-07-3

Barbeque Tips
by Raymond van Rijk
ISBN 978-1-905151-08-0

Dog Tips by Joe Inglis
ISBN 978-1-905151-09-7

Cat Tips by Joe Inglis
ISBN 978-1-905151-10-3

Baby & Toddler Tips
by Vicky Burford
ISBN 978-1-905151-11-0

Property Developing Tips
by F. Morgan & P Morgan
ISBN 978-1-905151-12-7

Personal Success Tips
by Brian Larcher
ISBN 978-1-905151-13-4

Genealogy Tips
by M. Vincent-Northam
ISBN 978-1-905151-22-6

Travel Tips
by Simon Worsfold
ISBN 978-1-905151-16-5

Podcasting Tips
by Malcolm Boyden
ISBN 978-1-905151-30-1

Sex Tips
by Julie Peasgood
ISBN 978-1-905151-25-7

Cricketing Tips
by R. Rotherham & G. Clifford
ISBN 978-1-905151-02-8

Horse & Pony Tips
by Joanne Bednall
ISBN 978-1-905151-19-6

Etiquette & Dining Tips
by Prof. R. Rotherham
ISBN 978-1-905151-21-9

Freelance Writing Tips
by Linda Jones
ISBN 978-1-905151-17-2

Retirement Tips
by Tony Rossiter
ISBN 978-1-905151-28-8

With many more to follow, these
books will form a useful compilation
for any bookshelf.

'The Greatest in the World' DVDs

The Greatest in the World – Gardening Tips
presented by Steve Brookes

The Greatest in the World – Yoga Tips
presented by David Gellineau and David Robson

The Greatest in the World – Cat & Kitten Tips
presented by Joe Inglis

The Greatest in the World – Dog & Puppy Tips
presented by Joe Inglis

For more information about currently available
and forthcoming book and DVD titles please visit:

www.**thegreatest**inthe**world**.com

or write to:

Public Eye Publications
PO Box 3182
Stratford-upon-Avon
Warwickshire CV37 7XW
United Kingdom

Tel / Fax: +44(0)1789 299616
Email: info@publiceyepublications.co.uk

The author

Julie Peasgood's acting career has spanned over thirty years of prestigious theatre and TV, ranging from innocent heroines at the Royal Shakespeare Company to playing a stripper in ITV's *September Song*. Her best known work, though, has been in Soaps, most notably *Brookside*, *Emmerdale* and *Hollyoaks*.

She is also a popular TV presenter, with numerous credits including *Good Food Live*, *Turf Wars*, *This Morning*, *Bootsale Challenge* and *Loose Women*.

Julie has written about travel, lifestyle and health for *The Daily Express*, *Woman's Journal*, *Slimmer Magazine* and the *Mail on Sunday*.

In 2004 Julie won the Royal Television Society 'Television Personality of the Year' award.

The Greatest Sex Tips in the World is her first book.

For more information about Julie, visit her website at **www.juliepeasgood.com**